GETTING STARTED IN
PRACTICAL ELECTRONICS

D1649396

Other Titles of Interest

BP121 How to Design and Make Your Own PCBs

BP266 Electronic Modules and Systems for Beginners

BP273 Practical Electronic Sensors

BP299 Practical Electronic Filters

BP316 Practical Electronic Design Data

BP317 Practical Electronic Timing

BP324 The Art of Soldering

BP332 A Beginners Guide to TTL Digital ICs

BP333 A Beginners Guide to CMOS Digital ICs

BP335 Operational Amplifier User's Handbook

BP378 45 Simple Electronic Terminal Block Projects

BP379 30 Simple IC Terminal Block Projects

BP392 Electronic Project Building for Beginners

BP410 35 Opto-Display Terminal Block Projects

BP432 Simple Sensor Terminal Block Projects

GETTING STARTED IN
PRACTICAL ELECTRONICS

by

Owen Bishop

BERNARD BABANI (publishing) LTD
THE GRAMPIANS
SHEPHERDS BUSH ROAD
LONDON W6 7NF
ENGLAND

Please Note

Although every care has been taken with the production of this book to ensure that any projects, designs, modifications and/or programs etc. contained herewith, operate in a correct and safe manner and also that all components specified are normally available in Great Britain, the Publishers and Author do not accept responsibility in any way for the failure, including fault in design, of any project, design, modification or program to work correctly or to cause damage to any other equipment that it may be connected to or used in conjunction with, or in respect of any other damage or injury that may be so caused, nor do the Publishers accept responsibility in any way for the failure to obtain specified components.

Notice is also given that if equipment that is still under warranty is modified in any way or used or connected with home-built equipment then that warranty may be void.

Due to the printing processes used in the production of this book, the absolute accuracy of the dimensions of the PCB patterns shown can not be guaranteed and should be regarded as a guide only.

First Published – November 1994
Reprinted – January 1998

British Library Cataloguing in Publication Data
    Bishop, O. N.
        Getting Started in Practical Electronics
        I. Title
        621.381

    ISBN 0 85934 345 6

Printed and Bound in Great Britain by Cox & Wyman Ltd, Reading

Introduction

This book is divided into two parts. In the first part we give all the information you need to get started in practical electronics. This is intended for the absolute beginner. It tells you all you need to know in order to build the 30 projects in the second part of the book. It describes electronic components: what they look like, how to handle them, what to ask for when you buy them, and a little about what they do. It explains how to understand circuit diagrams and how some of the simpler circuits operate. It shows you how to perform the simple calculations that you may sometimes need for making a circuit work exactly as you want it to. It gives detailed instructions for several different constructional techniques and shows you how to trouble-shoot the finished project.

The 30 projects in the second part of the book are divided into three chapters, each containing 10 projects. The projects are all suited to the beginner, but those in the first chapter are very easy, while those in the third chapter are slightly more difficult. All of the projects are powered by batteries, so there is no danger from electric shocks.

Electrical Units

The three main units used in electronics are:

Ampere (symbol, A) is the unit for measuring the flow of electric charge, or *current*. The name is very often shortened to *amp*. 1A = 1000mA (milliamp), 1mA = 1000μA (micro-amp).

Volt (symbol, V) is the unit for measuring the force which drives a current around a circuit. 1V = 1000mV (millivolt).

Ohm (symbol, Ω) is the unit for measuring the *resistance* to the flow of a current through a conductor. 1000Ω = 1kΩ (kilohm), 1000kΩ = 1MΩ (megohm).

CONTENTS

                                                        Page

Introduction v

Electrical Units vi

**Part A — ESSENTIALS OF ELECTRONICS
CONSTRUCTION** 1

   Chapter 1: Components 3
   Chapter 2: Ohm's Law 27
   Chapter 3: Circuits 31
   Chapter 4: Putting Things Together 39
   Chapter 5: Trouble-shooting 61

Part B — PROJECTS TO BUILD 67

   Chapter 6: Ten First Projects 69
     Project 1 — Moisture Detector 69
     Project 2 — Transistor Tester 71
     Project 3 — Remote-reading Thermometer 73
     Project 4 — Glittering Party-wear 77
     Project 5 — Intruder Detector 80
     Project 6 — Musical Box 83
     Project 7 — Electronic Handkerchief Knot 85
     Project 8 — Tooth-cleaner's Timer 87
     Project 9 — Door Alert 91
     Project 10 — Tantalizing Toss-up 92
   Chapter 7: Ten Easy Projects 97
     Project 11 — Timer Bar 97
     Project 12 — Christmas Star 103
     Project 13 — Fire Alarm 107
     Project 14 — Night Light 110
     Project 15 — Space Gun 115
     Project 16 — Are you alert? 118
     Project 17 — Blinkers 123
     Project 18 — Frost Detector 125
     Project 19 — Voltmeter Probe 129
     Project 20 — Master—slave Intercom 133

		Page
Chapter 8: Ten Challenging Projects	. . . .	139
Project 21 — Lie Detector	. . . .	139
Project 22 — Twisty Wire	. . . .	143
Project 23 — Spooky	. . . .	149
Project 24 — Remote Robot Control	. . . .	152
Project 25 — Mini Organ	. . . .	159
Project 26 — Nail and Cable Detector	. . . .	164
Project 27 — Sound-operated Switch	. . . .	167
Project 28 — Electronic Sculpture	. . . .	172
Project 29 — Two-tone Sounder	. . . .	178
Project 30 — Party Meter	. . . .	181
Appendix — NAMES AND ADDRESSES OF SUPPLIERS	. . . .	189

Part A

ESSENTIALS OF ELECTRONICS CONSTRUCTION

Chapter 1

COMPONENTS

It will help you to understand the descriptions, and also to purchase the components you will need, if you obtain one or more catalogues from mail order suppliers of electronic components. Some addresses are given in the Appendix.

Cells and Batteries

Cells are used for driving an electric current through a circuit; the ability of a cell to do this is rated in *volts* (see page vi). A typical dry cell, as used in an ordinary torch, produces a voltage of 1.5V when it is fresh. If we connect two such cells together *in series*, as in Figure 1, we have a *battery*. Its driving force is 3V. Similarly, three cells produce 4.5V, four cells produce 6V (Fig. 2) and six cells produce 9V. We usually make up a battery by clipping 2 or more cells into a plastic *battery holder*. This contains springs to hold the cells in place

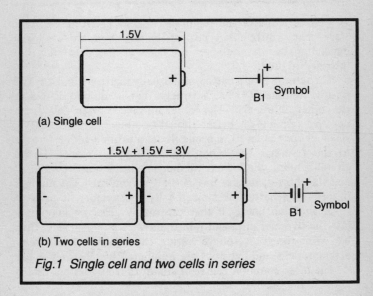

(a) Single cell

(b) Two cells in series

Fig.1 Single cell and two cells in series

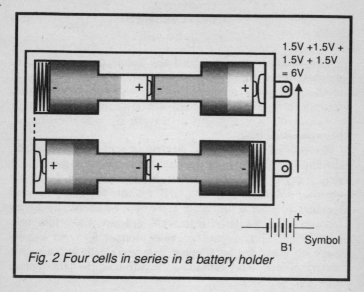

1.5V +1.5V +
1.5V + 1.5V
= 6V

+

B1   Symbol

Fig. 2 Four cells in series in a battery holder

as well as to make the required contacts between the cells. Very many different types of battery box are available, depending on the number and size of the cells they are intended to hold.

The terminals of a battery are usually marked + and −. The positive terminal (+) has a voltage that is positive of that at the other terminal. The other terminal, often called the negative terminal, is better thought to be at zero volts (0V), since all voltage levels in a circuit are measured with reference to this terminal, the *ground* voltage for the circuit. In the circuit symbol, the longer, thinner line is the positive terminal and the shorter, thicker line is the 0V terminal. The number of cells in a battery is indicated by the number of pairs of thick and thin lines. If there are many cells, we may draw just the two end ones and join them with a dashed line; then we write the total voltage beside the symbol. In a circuit diagram, cells and batteries are numbered B1, B2, and so on.

The most common cell sizes are indicated by letters. Starting with the smallest:

4

AAA	miniature pen-light cells
AA	pen-light cells
C	small torch cells
D	large torch cells

Sizes AAA and AA are suitable for projects that take a small amount of current, or are never left switched on for long periods. They are useful when a project case is small and intended to be hand-held. Sizes C and D are better for projects requiring larger currents or that are run continuously for days or weeks.

The cheapest cells of any given size are carbon-zinc cells, but they do not last as long as alkaline cells, which are more expensive. In the long run, the cheapest type of cell is the nickel-cadmium (Nicad) cell. This is more expensive to buy than the other types but, even taking into account the cost of a charger, they can be used and recharged several hundred times. Nicad cells typically have a voltage of 1.2V, which means that we need to connect *five* Nicad cells in series to obtain the equivalent of four carbon-zinc or alkaline cells. Usually we do not bother to do this, as most circuits work just as well on 4.8V. However, to maximise the volume of sound or the brightness of lamps in certain circuits, connect a fifth Nicad in series with a four-cell battery holder.

Instead of using a battery holder with separate cells, you can buy cells already connected, sold as a battery or power-pack. These are available in a range of voltages, such as 3V, 4.5V, 6V, 9V and 12V. The PP3 battery is a small 9V battery which is particularly useful for hand-held or compact projects. It is the sort sold for electronic clocks, radios and kitchen balances.

The PP3 battery and the AA size battery holders are provided with a pair of male and female contacts. *Battery clips* fix on to these and have a pair of wires (usually one red for positive and one black for 0V) to connect to the circuit. Larger battery holders have metal tags to which connecting wires are soldered. If a soldering iron is not available, just twist the ends of the wires several times around the tags.

Wire

For most connections we use PVC-covered copper wire, preferably the sort which is tinned to protect it from corrosion and to make it easier to solder. The most suitable wire for circuit-board work is single-stranded or single-core wire. It is usually described as 1/0.6 wire, meaning one strand 0.6mm in diameter, and is sometimes called *bell wire*. This is essential for building circuits on a bread-board (p.39). It is sometimes specified by its gauge, which is 22 SWG (standard wire gauge). For connecting off-board components such as batteries or loudspeakers to the circuit board, it is preferable to use a more flexible multi-stranded wire. A suitable kind is 7/0.2 (seven strands 0.2mm diam) PVC-covered wire, sometimes known as *hook-up wire*. A 10m coil of each kind of wire in two colours (say red and blue) is enough for building all the projects in this book. A wire stripper is extremely useful for cutting the wire to the required lengths and for stripping off the insulation at its ends. The cheapest model is good enough for work on these projects; before buying one, check that it will strip narrow-gauge (22 SWG) wire; some models are intended only for use by electricians with mains cables.

Switches

The kind of switch most frequently used in this book is the *single-pole single throw switch* (SPST) represented by the symbol shown in Figure 3. It has one pair of contacts which

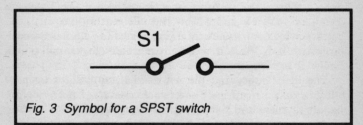

Fig. 3 Symbol for a SPST switch

are either open or closed. There are three forms. A *toggle switch* has a lever which is pushed one way or the other to open or close the switch. A *slide switch* has a sliding knob, and a *rocker switch* is activated by a rocker which has two positions. A single-pole double throw (SPDT) switch allows one terminal to be put into contact with either of the other two. This is also known as a *change-over switch*. Sometimes we need to be able to switch two circuits simultaneously and use double-pole switches, either single throw (DPST) or double throw (DPDT). When purchasing switches it is important to be sure that they will stand up to the voltages and currents they are likely to experience. This is not a problem in this book as all voltages and currents are low.

For instantaneous connections we use a push-button switch (Fig.4). Most often we use a *push-to-make* type in which the contacts are normally open and close when the button is pressed. Occasionally a *push-to-break* type is required.

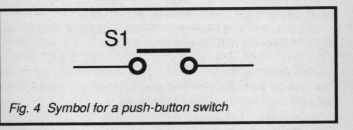

Fig. 4 Symbol for a push-button switch

Other types of switch include *microswitches*, which are operated by very small pressures applied to a lever or button and *tilt switches*, which are closed when the body of the switch is upright but open when it is tilted. The latter are often used in security applications to detect motion.

A *relay* is a switch that is opened or closed electro-magnetically. When a current passes through the coil of the relay, it attracts an armature, made from magnetic material. Movement of the armature causes the contacts to open or close; often a relay has *change-over contacts* (Fig.5). Before purchasing a relay, make sure that it is intended to operate at the voltage of your circuit; usually a range is quoted, such as 4.5V−7.5V. It is also important to be certain that the relay contacts are rated to withstand the expected voltages and currents in the relay-switched circuit, otherwise sparking at the contacts may cause them to become permanently fused together. This is not likely to be a problem with the circuits

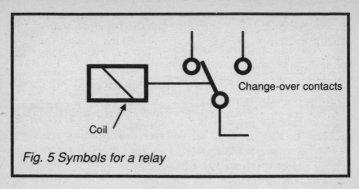

Fig. 5 Symbols for a relay

Coil

Change-over contacts

in this book. For small-scale work, very small miniature or sub-miniature relays are available, suitable for mounting on stripboard or a pcb (printed circuit board, see p.53).

Switches on a circuit diagram are numbered S1, S2 and so on. Relays are numbered RLA1, RLA2.

Sockets and Plugs

The type of socket most often used in the projects are sockets for integrated circuits (ics, p.23). These are of the type known as *dual-in-line* (DIL) because they have two parallel rows of sockets for the pins that are found on the long edges of the ic. The pins are spaced 2.5mm apart and two rows are 10mm apart. Sockets are made for 8, 14, 16 or 18 pins. They are also made for ics with many more pins than this, though ics with more than 18 pins are not used in this book. For ics with more pins, the rows are usually further apart.

Although it is possible to solder an ic directly to the stripboard or pcb, it is better to solder a socket to the board and insert the ic in this after the connections to the circuit have been tested. Once an ic has been soldered in, it is very hard to get it out again, and it is likely to be damaged by the heat of the soldering iron. But, if a fault is suspected in the circuit, it is easy to remove an ic from its socket, to test it, and also the parts of the circuit which link up with the ic. To help you when ordering ic sockets, the number of pins on each type of ic is listed on pages 24–25.

There are dozens of different kinds of socket for other purposes. One of the most generally useful types is known as a *terminal post*. It is mounted on the panel or wall of the circuit enclosure. It has a screw-top which secures the bare ends of connection wires. It incorporates a 4mm socket for taking 4mm *wander plugs*.

It is also possible to buy plain 4mm sockets, which are cheaper than the terminal posts.

Sockets on a circuit diagram are numbered with the prefix SKT.

Resistors

A resistor offers resistance to the flow of an electric current. Its resistance is measured in *ohms, kilohms* or *megohms* (p.vi). A typical resistor consists of a cylindrical ceramic body with terminal wires at either end (Fig.6a). Various types are

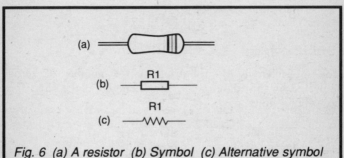

Fig. 6 (a) A resistor (b) Symbol (c) Alternative symbol

manufactured but the 0.6W metal film resistor is recommended for these projects. These have a *tolerance* of ±1%. This means that the actual value of the resistor is within 1% of its marked value. For example, if its marked value is 100Ω, its actual resistance is between 99Ω and 101Ω. The value of a resistor is usually marked on its body by a set of coloured rings (Fig.7). The colours correspond to numbers:

black	= 0	green	= 5
brown	= 1	blue	= 6
red	= 2	violet	= 7
orange	= 3	grey	= 8
yellow	= 4	white	= 9

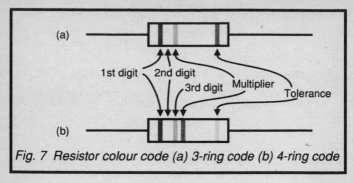

Fig. 7 Resistor colour code (a) 3-ring code (b) 4-ring code

There are two systems for coding resistance. One system uses three rings:

> 1 first digit
> 2 second digit
> 3 multiplier

The multiplier is '1' followed by the number of zeroes indicated by the colour code. For example, if the three rings are yellow, violet, red:

First digit is:	yellow = 4
Second digit is:	violet = 7
Multiplier is:	red = 100 (two zeroes)

The resistance is $47 \times 100 = 4700\Omega$, or $4.7k\Omega$. In the four-ring system, the first *three* rings are the first three digits, and the *fourth* is the multiplier. In this system a $4.7k\Omega$ resistor is marked:

> yellow = 4
> violet = 7
> black = 0
> brown = 10 (one zero)

$$470 \times 10 = 4700k\Omega \text{ or } 4.7k\Omega.$$

For low-value resistors we have two further multiplier codes for the last (third or fourth) ring:

gold = multiply by 0.1
silver = multiply by 0.01

A resistor marked yellow, violet, gold has a resistance 47 × 0.1 = 4.7Ω.

Reading the colour rings is not as difficult as it might seem because only a few combinations of colours commonly occur. Resistors are made with a few standard values:

10   12   15   18   22   27   33   39   47   56   68   82

after this, the sequence repeats with the same numbers multiplied by 10:

100 120 150 180 220 270 330 390 470 560 680 820

Then we get to the kilohm ranges: 1000, 1200, 1500, and so on. This continues to higher resistances, the top value usually being 10MΩ. The advantage is that there are only 12 possible combinations of colours to look out for in the first two digits:

10 = brown, black	12 = brown, red	15 = brown, green
18 = brown, grey	22 = red, red	27 = red, violet
33 = orange, orange	39 = orange, white	47 = yellow, violet
56 = green, blue	68 = blue, grey	82 = grey, red

With a little practice, you will be able to recognise these pairs of colours and then multiply by the appropriate multiplier. The set of values listed above is known as the E12 series. For greater precision there is a set of values, the E24 series with resistances in between the E12 set. The only two E24 resistors used in this book are 240kΩ and 910kΩ.

The tolerance of a resistor is indicated by an additional coloured ring, usually at the other end of the resistor. The colour codes for tolerance are:

brown = ±1%   red = ±2%   gold = ±5%   silver = ±10%

In circuit diagrams, resistors are numbered R2, R2, etc. We have a short-hand way of indicating the values of resistors, and the resistances of other components such as loudspeakers and the coils of relays. We omit the ohm symbol, but use k and M to represent kilohms and megohms. The k or M can be used in place of a decimal point. Examples:

220 means 220Ω	560 means 560Ω
220k means 220kΩ	1M means 1MΩ
4k7 means 4.7kΩ	3M3 means 3.3MΩ

For resistances less than 10 ohms, we use R as the decimal point:

$$5R6 \text{ means } 5.6Ω.$$

As well as the fixed resistors described above, a circuit may contain some variable resistors. One type, known as a *rotary potentiometer* (or often more briefly as a 'pot'), is used when we may want to change the value of a resistance frequently, for example for controlling the volume of sound from a loudspeaker, or in the mechanism of a computer joystick. Figure 8 shows a pot as seen from the 'front', which is the side nearest to the panel when it is mounted. Inside the cylindrical metal case is the resistive part of the pot. This is an almost complete circle of carbon-base 'track' with terminals connected to both ends (a and b in the figure). There is a contact, known as a *wiper*, which can be rotated to move along the track. Its terminal is labelled w in the figure. The wiper is turned by twisting the plastic shaft; generally we fix a plastic knob to the shaft to make it easier to adjust. Cermet

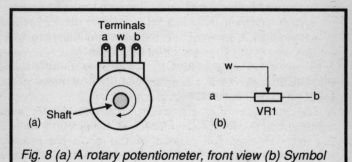

Fig. 8 (a) A rotary potentiometer, front view (b) Symbol

12

pots have their tracks made of ceramic material; they are more expensive than the carbon type but more hard-wearing. Carbon tracked pots are suitable for all the projects in this book, and all are of the *linear* type, in which equal amounts of turn of the shaft produce equal amounts of change of resistance.

Another type of variable resistor is the *preset*, also known as a *trimpot*. This type is used when a resistance has to be set to a particular value once and for all when setting up a circuit, or perhaps readjusted very infrequently. It is essentially the same as a pot, but smaller, and is usually adjusted by using a screwdriver. For the projects in this book, use miniature carbon presets or sub-miniature cermet presets; both types are cheap. Presets are available in vertical or horizontal form; we have used the horizontal form, which has pins spaced as shown in Figure 9.

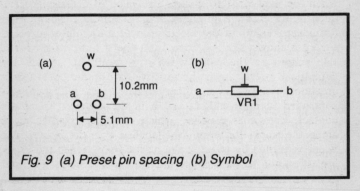

Fig. 9 (a) Preset pin spacing (b) Symbol

A *light-dependent resistor* (LDR), also known as a *photoconductive cell* (PCC) is made from a material which becomes less resistive in the light (Fig.10). A typical example of this is the ORP12, which has a resistance of 1MΩ or more in the dark, but only about 80Ω in bright light.

The resistance of a *thermistor* varies considerably with temperature, so we use thermistors as temperature sensors. The type required for projects in this book has *negative temperature coefficient* (ntc), which means that its resistance *decreases* as temperature *increases*. A thermistor (Fig.11) may

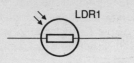

Fig. 10 Symbol for a light-dependent resistor

Fig. 11 Symbol for a thermistor (n.t.c.)

consist of a disc or bead of material with two terminal wires. The thermistor specified for Project 3, for example, has a resistance of 500Ω at 25°C. As the thermistor is cooled to 0°C, the resistance increases to about 1700Ω.

Capacitors

A capacitor is a device for storing electric charge. The amount of charge it stores is determined by its *capacitance*. Capacitance is measured in *farads* (symbol, F) but this unit is far too large for practical purposes. Instead, we use the *microfarad* (symbol, μF), which is one-millionth of a farad. We also use smaller units:

nanofarad (symbol, nF)
equal to one-thousandth of a microfarad

picofarad (symbol, pF)
equal to one-thousandth of a nanofarad

A capacitor consists of two metal plates or films with a non-conducting material (the *dielectric*) between them. This is indicated by the symbol for the capacitor (Fig.12). The capacitance depends partly on the area of the metal plates or films. Polystyrene capacitors consist of two sheets of aluminium

14

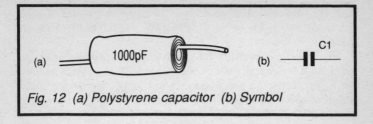

Fig. 12 (a) Polystyrene capacitor (b) Symbol

foil tightly rolled for compactness, with thin layers of the
plastic polystyrene to stop the turns of the foil from touching.   A terminal wire is connected to each sheet of foil.
Polystyrene capacitors are made with capacitances in the range
of a few picofarads up to about 47nF.   For most of the
circuits in this book we use *metallised polyester film* capacitors, which are inexpensive and available with capacitances
from 1nF up to 2.2μF.   Another suitable and inexpensive
type is the *mylar film* capacitor.

For higher capacitances we generally use *aluminium
electrolytic* capacitors.   These range from 0.1μF up to
10000μF. The insulating layer in these capacitors consists of
a thin layer of aluminium oxide formed on the plates by
passing a current through the capacitor when it is manufactured. This means that the capacitor is polarised (Fig.13). It

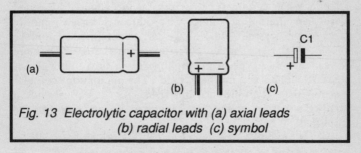

*Fig. 13 Electrolytic capacitor with (a) axial leads
(b) radial leads (c) symbol*

must always be connected so that the positive lead is at a
higher voltage than the negative lead. Usually the negative
lead is marked with a bold negative sign. Always check that
the capacitor is connected with the correct polarity. If it is
not, the film of oxide will be gradually destroyed. This will

15

ruin the capacitor and — worse — after a few minutes of such treatment, it is likely to EXPLODE. This could cause an injury.

Electrolytic capacitors are made with either radial leads or axial leads. Generally we prefer those with axial leads as they are easier to use on breadboards and stripboard. Occasionally we have specified radial leads where space is scarce on a pcb.

Inductors

An inductor is a coil of wire, usually wound around a core of magnetic material. The core may be iron, but often is a special ceramic material, known as *ferrite*. Rods of ferrite are used as aerials in portable radio sets, with tuning coils wound round them. Another use for an inductor is to prevent rapid changes in the size and direction of currents; in this application the inductor is called a *choke*. Its ability to do this is related to its *inductance*. Inductance is measured in *henries* (symbol, H). The inductance of most practical inductors is measured in millihenries (symbol, mH) or in microhenries (symbol, μH).

Microphones

These generate a voltage (usually only a few millivolts) when they pick up sound vibrations. Some rely on the *piezo-electric effect*. When certain types of crystal are vibrated by sound waves, an alternating voltage is produced between opposite faces of the crystal. This voltage can be amplified to produce an electrical signal which corresponds to the original sound waves. Another type of microphone has a tiny coil, which is made to vibrate in a magnetic field. The microphone contains a strong magnet to produce this field. As the coil vibrates, a small alternating voltage is generated in it; this can be amplified.

A microphone which operates on this principle is called a *moving coil* microphone or a *dynamic* microphone.

Both types of microphone are usually enclosed in a protective case which also makes them easy to handle. The instrument may be mounted on a stand. But the electronically active part of the microphone, the *microphone insert*, is all that is really necessary. An insert costs much less than a complete microphone and is perfectly adequate for the circuits of this book.

Audio Output Devices

Sounders: These consist of a thin sheet of piezoelectric material mounted on a thin metal plate. Their action is the reverse of that of the crystal microphone; when an alternating voltage is applied to the sounder, it vibrates and produces sound. Note that a sounder requires a driving circuit to produce the alternating voltage. Sounders are labelled XTAL1, etc. in circuit diagrams.

AWDs: Audible warning devices have a built-in oscillator to generate the alternating voltage; they sound whenever a voltage is applied to them. There are various types, including those which emit a buzzing sound and those which emit various high-pitched whistles and bleeps. Some of them produce two-tone sounds and others wail like a siren. They produce a very loud sound, even though the current they require is only a few milliamps. The larger models are suitable as alarms for security systems. Most of them work on a wide range of voltages, such as 6V to 12V. In the circuits of this book, any type can be used, provided it has a suitable working voltage.

Loudspeakers: These are available in a wide range of sizes; in general, the larger the diameter the better the quality of the sound, particularly in the bass region. But, for the projects in this book a low-cost speaker up to about 90mm diameter will be entirely suitable. It may be important to use one of small diameter, say 38mm, so that it will fit into a small enclosure. The most important point to note is that loudspeakers fall into two main categories, low coil resistance (typically 8Ω) and high coil resistance (typically 64Ω). The circuit may not work if the wrong kind is used.

With all kinds of audible device the volume of sound produced is very much reduced if the device is not firmly fixed to the equipment enclosure. Figure 55, page 83, shows how to mount a piezo-electric sounder. AWDs usually have a pair of lugs for bolting the device to the panel. Figure 14 shows how to mount a small loudspeaker if it does not have holes in its frame for bolts.

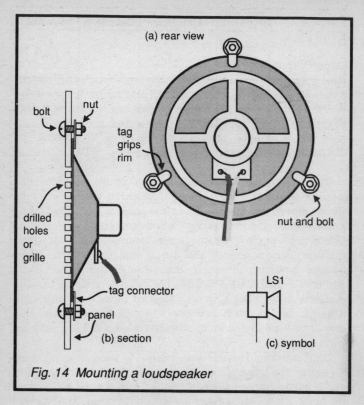

Fig. 14 Mounting a loudspeaker

Semiconductors

These are devices based on one of several types of *semiconducting material*. The special properties of semiconductors are the basis of modern electronics. Figure 15 shows the semiconductors used in this book and their symbols.

Diodes: A diode has two terminals known as the *anode* and the *cathode*. The diode allows current to flow freely in *one direction only*, from anode to cathode. A typical and frequently used diode is type number 1N4148. In this, the semiconducting material is based on silicon, but diodes can also be based on another semiconductor, germanium. The OA47 diode is an example of a germanium diode. A diode is usually marked with a band at one end to indicate which is the

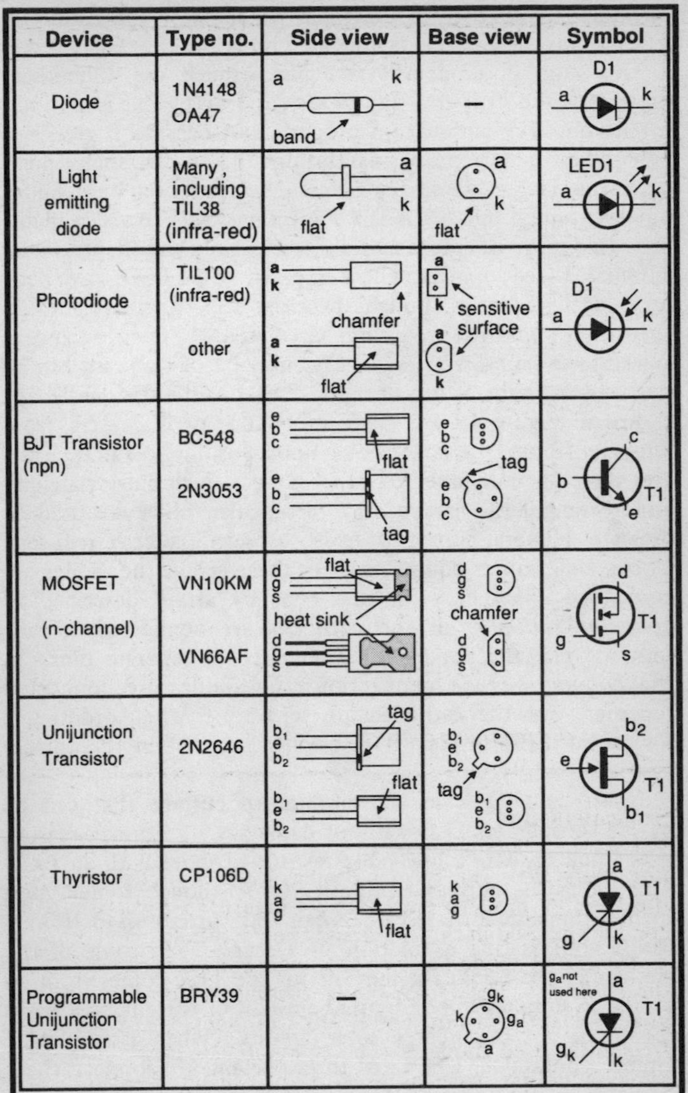

Device	Type no.	Side view	Base view	Symbol
Diode	1N4148 OA47	a — k, band	—	D1, a ▶ k
Light emitting diode	Many, including TIL38 (infra-red)	a, k, flat	a, k, flat	LED1, a ▶ k
Photodiode	TIL100 (infra-red) / other	a, k, chamfer / a, k, flat	a, k, sensitive surface / a, k	D1, a ▶ k
BJT Transistor (npn)	BC548 / 2N3053	e b c, flat / e b c, tag	e b c, tag / e b c	b, c, e, T1
MOSFET (n-channel)	VN10KM / VN66AF	d g s, flat / d g s, heat sink	d g s, chamfer / d g s	d, g, s, T1
Unijunction Transistor	2N2646	b_1 e b_2, tag / b_1 e b_2, flat	b_1 e b_2, tag / b_1 e b_2	b_2, e, b_1, T1
Thyristor	CP106D	k a g, flat	k a g	a, g, k, T1
Programmable Unijunction Transistor	BRY39	—	g_k, g_a, a	g_a not used here, a, g_k, k, T1

Fig. 15 Semiconductor devices

cathode. Note that in diagrams we indicate the anode by letter a, but the cathode is indicated by letter k.

One kind of diode that we make much use of in these projects is the *light-emitting diode* (or LED). This is used not for its one-way conduction property but because it gives out light when a current passes through it. LEDs make good indicating lamps. Ordinary filament lamps (torch bulbs) burn out eventually, but LEDs last a lot longer. LEDs are available in a wide range of colours, brightnesses, sizes and shapes. Their colours are red, orange, yellow or green. Blue LEDs have been introduced recently, though these are still expensive. LEDs that emit infra-red radiation are used in remote control systems, as in Project 24. LEDs may be of standard brightness, super-bright or ultra-bright. LEDs of the standard shape shown in Figure 15 are made in a range of diameters, from 3mm to 10mm, the latter being known as jumbo LEDs. They are made in a number of other shapes, including triangular and rectangular. Arrays of 7 rectangular LEDs are used to indicate numerals from 0 to 9, as seen on cash registers, clocks and similar equipment. In these arrays the diodes are connected together. In one type of array, described as *common cathode*, all the cathodes are connected to one terminal pin; the anodes are connected to separate pins. In the *common anode* connection, the anodes are connected together, but the cathodes are separate. When ordering a 7-segment LED display it is essential to obtain the correct type.

There is a limit to the amount of current that can be passed through an LED without damaging it. For this reason, it is usual to wire a low-value resistor in series with an LED. This limits the current to about 20mA, though some types, such as the large infra-red LEDs can take current up to 100mA for periods lasting a fraction of a second. In some of the circuits in the book, the current for the LED comes from an ic; the ic supplies only a limited amount of current, so a series resistor is not required in such circuits. When assembling a circuit containing LEDs, it is important to connect them correctly so that current flows in at the anode and out at the cathode. If it is connected the other way round, no current flows and no light is produced. Usually the anode wire of the

LED is longer than that of the cathode. In some types the rim is flattened on the cathode side, as shown in Figure 15. If, when you are testing a circuit, an LED does not light when it should, check that it is connected the right way round. But note that although LEDs have the diode property of allowing only one-way current, unlike ordinary diodes, they can not withstand a large voltage in the reverse direction. A voltage of about 6V or more applied in the wrong direction is likely to burn out the LED.

Another type of diode is the *photodiode*. Actually, ordinary diodes too are sensitive to light, but they are usually enclosed in an opaque package to prevent light reaching them. Photodiodes have a glass package. In most applications, they are connected so that the cathode is *positive* of the anode, which means that they do not conduct. But in fact there is a very small *leakage current* flowing from cathode to anode. This current varies with the amount of light falling on the diode, so the diode is used as a light sensor. Photodiodes are sensitive to ordinary light and there are special types sensitive to infra red, as used in Project 24.

Finally, there are the *flashing LEDs*. These look like ordinary LEDs but they include a tiny circuit which flashes them on and off, usually about once a second. These LEDs operate on a higher voltage (usually 6V) and do not require a series resistor. This completes the survey of LEDs — there are very many types, and we use almost all of them in this book.

Transistors: When we use the term 'transistor', without saying what *sort* of transistor, we usually mean a *bipolar junction transistor* (BJT). These are of two kinds, known as *npn* and *pnp*, depending on their structure. In this book we use only the npn kind, and of these we use only two types, the BC548 general-purpose transistor, and the 2N3053, which is intended for a larger current and is described as a driver transistor. But both types have the same structure and work in the same way. A transistor has three terminals known as the collector (c), the base (b) and the emitter (e). In most applications the emitter is connected to 0V. A small current is made to flow into the base, from where it flows to the emitter and out to the 0V line (Fig.16). The collector is

21

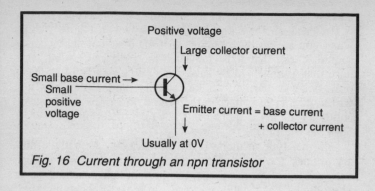

Fig. 16 Current through an npn transistor

positive with respect to the emitter but no current flows
from collector to emitter if there is no base current. When a
base current flows, a collector current flows too. The important property of a transistor is that the collector current is
many times larger than the base current, often several hundred
times larger. In the BC548 it is about 500 times larger; we say
that the *gain* of the BC548 is 500. Whatever the amount of
the base current, the collector current is 500 times larger;
the transistor acts as a *current amplifier*. If the base current
is zero, the collector current is zero; we say that the transistor
is *turned off*, like a switch. If the base current is increased,
the collector current increases in proportion. If the base
current is greater than a certain amount, the collector current
reaches a maximum value; the transistor is *saturated*. We say
that the transistor is *turned on*. So a transistor may be used
either as an *amplifier* or as a *switch*. We shall see examples of
both these uses in the projects.

   MOSFETs: These are a kind of *field effect transistor*.
Their terminals are known as the drain (d), gate (g) and source
(s). The MOSFETs used in this book are of the type known as
n-channel, and correspond to npn BJTs. They are connected
in the same way as BJTs with the source, gate and drain
corresponding to the emitter, base and collector respectively.
The main difference in their action is that the gate is insulated
from the rest of the transistor, so that virtually no current can
flow into it. But the *voltage* at the gate controls the *current*
flowing in at the drain and out at the source. This may sound

wrong, which is because we are referring to *conventional current*, said to flow from positive to negative. In fact, current in a metallic conductor and in n-type semiconductors is a flow of electrons (negative charge) from *negative to positive*. The source terminal is the source of electrons entering the MOSFET and they drain away toward the positive supply line through the drain. But most people prefer to stay with the idea of conventional current, from drain to source. One reason for using MOSFETs is that they require no current to control them so are useful in circuits where practically no current is available. Like BJTs, MOSFETs are used as amplifiers or as switches.

Unijunction transistors: BJTs have two base terminals (b_1 and b_2) and an emitter. They are useful for building simple oscillator circuits (p.70).

Thyristors: As its circuit symbol shows, a thyristor has the one-way properties of a diode, but current does not flow at all unless the thyristor is triggered into action. This is done by applying a short positive pulse to its gate terminal (g). The current flows from anode (a) to cathode (k). Current continues to flow for as long as the circuit supplies more than a certain minimum current, known as the *holding current.* This is usually about 5mA (p.vi), more with some types. If the holding current falls below 5mA, the thyristor stops conducting altogether. It then requires another positive pulse at its gate to start it conducting again.

Programmable UJTs: This is a four-terminal device, with an anode, cathode, anode gate (g_a) and cathode gate (g_k). The PUJT can be used in several different ways, but in this book we use it in the same way as a thyristor. The anode gate is not used. A positive pulse is supplied to the cathode gate to make the UJT conduct. The holding current is about $250\mu A$ (p.vi).

Integrated Circuits

These consist of a number of miniature transistors, resistors and capacitors manufactured on a single chip of silicon so that they are already connected as a circuit or part of a circuit. The ic is usually housed in a package of the kind shown in Figure 17, though the number of terminal pins may range

23

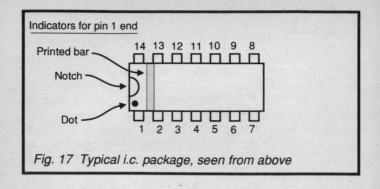

Fig. 17 Typical i.c. package, seen from above

from 8 to 40. By using the ready-connected circuits in ics, we are able to build complicated circuits by making just a few connections to the pins. This makes it easier for the beginner to construct circuits that do useful and interesting things. Below we list all the ics used in this book, by type number. In brackets we state the number of terminal pins; this information is supplied for use when you are ordering ic sockets (p.8). The action of the ics is outlined in the project descriptions.

Amplifier ics:
   LF351 Operational amplifier (8)
   ICL7611 Operational amplifier (8)
   TL046 Quadruple operational amplifier (16)

Timer ics:
   7555 General purpose timer (8)
   7556 Dual general purpose timer (14)
   ZN1034 Precision counter-timer (14)

Logic ics:
   4011 Quadruple 2-input NAND gate (14)
   4020 14-stage counter (16)
   4021 8-stage shift register (16)
   4027 Dual J-K flip-flop (16)
   4046 Phase locked loop (16)
   4049 Hex inverting buffer gate (16)

4081 Quadruple 2-input AND gate (14)
40110 Decade up-down counter (16)
74HC00 Quadruple 2-input NAND gate (14)
74HC164 8-stage shift register (14)

Special function ics:
UM66 Melody generator (3, see Fig.18)
CS209 Proximity detector (8)
UM3561 Sound effects generator (8)
3915 Bargraph display, logarithmic (18)
LM3909 LED flasher (8)
7760 Voltage converter (8)
TDA8160 Infra-red remote receiver (8)

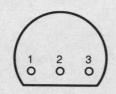

Fig. 18 Package of UM66, seen from below

Where the type number does not have any distinguishing code letters, it usually means that the same ic is made by several different manufacturers. In the catalogues you may find, for example, that the 7555 timer ic is sold under various type numbers such as ICM5777IPA and TL7555CP. It is the digits 7555 that identify the timer type.

The circuit symbol for an ic is usually a rectangle with connections to and from it; the pin numbers are written beside each connection. Operational amplifiers and logic gates have special symbols (Fig.19).

Most of the ics listed above are manufactured using CMOS technology. We are not concerned with the details of this, but there is one practical point that needs to be kept in mind. CMOS ics are liable to be damaged by electrostatic charges. They are supplied in plastic-topped packs with a metallised card base, or with their pins pushed into a small rectangle of

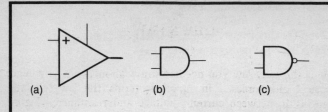

Fig.19 Symbols for (a) operational amplifier (b) 2-input AND gate, (c) 2-input NAND gate

black conductive foam. Leave them in their original packing until you are ready to use them. Electrostatic charges on the body are reduced by wearing clothes made from non-synthetic fibres, such as cotton and wool. Handle the ics as little as possible, and try not to touch their pins with your fingers. It is a good idea to touch an earthed metal object occasionally to discharge the body; do this especially before you need to handle an ic. A table lamp with an earthed metal base is a handy object to touch, but check that its metal parts are connected to the mains earth line, or wire a small rectangle of metal to a nearby cold water pipe, or to a metal spike pushed into damp soil outside the window, and place the plate on your workbench, where it is easy to reach. With these simple precautions it is very rarely that a CMOS ic will be damaged.

Chapter 2

OHM'S LAW

This is the only law you need to know about when you begin practical electronics. In practical terms the law tells the relationship between current, voltage and resistance. Figure 20 shows a resistor with:

a voltage V across it
a current I passing through it
a resistance R

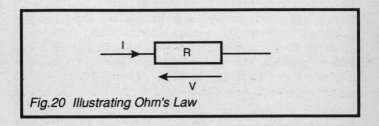

Fig.20 Illustrating Ohm's Law

The arrow indicating the voltage V points toward the positive end of the resistor, so the current I is flowing from left to right. If V is in volts, I is in amps and R is in ohms, the equation is:

$$V = IR$$

This equation is generally known as the *Ohm's Law equation*. It can be rearranged to give two other equivalent equations:

$$I = V/R \qquad R = V/I$$

These three equations show that, if you already know any *two* of the values V, I and R, you can always calculate the third value. For example:

If a current of 4A is passing through a 10Ω resistor, the voltage across it is $V = IR = 4 \times 10 = 40$V. Note that letter V is the symbol for the unit, the volt; letter V in italics is the symbol for 'a voltage'.

If a 100Ω resistor has a voltage of 40V across it, the current through it is $I = V/R = 40/100 = 0.4A$.

If a resistor with 9V across it has a current 0.25A through it, its resistance is $R = V/I = 9/0.25 = 36Ω$.

A useful consequence of the relationship between volts, amps, and ohms is illustrated by Figure 21. The total voltage across the two resistors is 6V. What is the voltage at point A where the resistors join?

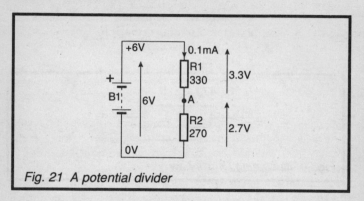

Fig. 21 A potential divider

The total of the two resistors is 330Ω + 270Ω = 600Ω. The same current flows through *both* resistors because it has nowhere else to go. This current is:

$$I = V/R = 6/600 = 0.01A, \text{ or } 10mA .$$

Taking the R1 alone, its resistance is 330Ω and the current through it is 0.01A. The voltage across it is:

$$V = IR = 0.01 \times 330 = 3.3V$$

Similarly, the voltage across R2 alone is:

$$V = IR = 0.01 \times 270 = 2.7V$$

The total voltage (or potential) across R1 and R2 is divided into two parts, 3.3V across R1 and 2.7V across R2. The pair of resistors act as a *potential divider*. The voltage across each resistor is proportional to its resistance. We use this fact in circuits when we have a voltage of a given size and wish to obtain a smaller one.

The general equation for calculating the voltage v from a potential divider (at point A), given the input voltage V is:

$$v = \frac{V \times R2}{R1 + R2}$$

For example, if V = 12V, R1 = 470Ω and R2 = 680Ω, then:

$$v = \frac{12 \times 680}{470 + 680} = 7.1V$$

The thing to watch for is that, if the circuit connected to point A draws too much current from the divider, some of the current that should have passed through R2 now passes out to the connected circuit. As a result, the voltage at A is lower, possibly much lower, than calculated. A general rule is to make sure that the current taken from point A is no more than one-tenth of the current flowing through the divider. In the example above, the total resistance is 1150Ω and the current through the divider is 12/1150 = 10.4mA. In this case we must not draw more than 1.04mA from point A. If we needed more current than this, we could reduce R1 and R2 to, say, 47Ω and 68Ω so that the current through the divider is 104mA and we can draw up to 10.4mA.

Chapter 3

CIRCUITS

Certain arrangements of components occur so often in several projects that we describe them here in this chapter. The way the components are connected together is shown in the *circuit diagram*, sometimes called a *schematic diagram*. Figure 22 is an example of a circuit diagram and shows how we often connect an npn transistor in a circuit. Note how we place a dot where two connections join. The emitter is connected directly to the 0V line. There is a resistor R1 in series with the base to limit the amount of current flowing to it. The values of the resistor is selected so that the amount of base current is just enough to make a collector current flow, but not enough to saturate (p.22) the transistor. We say that the base current *biases* the transistor into conduction. There is also a resistor R2 in series with the collector. When the collector current flows through this resistor a voltage appears across it. In many applications, the size of the collector current and the value of the resistor are such that the value across the resistor is about half the supply voltage. This means that if the base current is reduced slightly, the collector current is also reduced and the voltage across it is decreased. The voltage at the collector terminal rises slightly. Conversely, if the base current is increased slightly, the collector voltage falls.

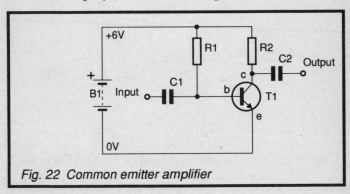

Fig. 22 Common emitter amplifier

The capacitors are used to couple this circuit to other circuits. An increase in voltage at the input terminal results in an additional flow of current from C1 to the base of the transistor. Similarly, a fall in input voltage diverts some of the current flowing through R1 to flow to C1, and so less current flows to the base. In this way an alternating voltage at the input makes the base current vary, and this causes variation in the voltage at the collector. This larger alternating voltage passes to the output through C2. Note that as the input voltage *rises*, the collector voltage *falls*, so this is an *inverting* amplifier. This way of using the transistor is known as the *common emitter* connection, because the emitter terminal is shared between both the input and output sides of the circuit. Figure 22 is a simple example of a common emitter amplifier.

In Projects 13 and 18 we use another connection, known as the *common collector* connection.

If we are using the transistor as a switch (p.22), there is usually no need for the capacitors or even for the base resistor. Circuits for this and for other semiconductor devices are described in the projects concerned.

A commonly used operational amplifier (op amp) circuit is shown in Figure 23. This is an *inverting amplifier*. It requires two power rails, usually referred to as +V and −V

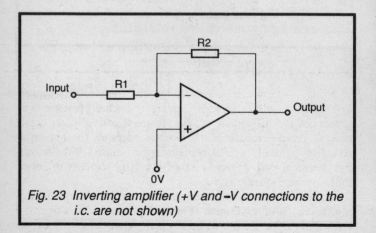

Fig. 23 Inverting amplifier (+V and −V connections to the
i.c. are not shown)

(Fig.101). The non-inverting input (+) is held at 0V. The input signal is connected through a resistor R1 to the inverting input (−) of the op amp. There is a feedback resistor R2. As the input voltage changes, the output voltage changes in the reverse direction, but by a bigger amount. The gain of the amplifier when connected in this way is:

$$gain = R2/R1$$

If R1 is 10kΩ for example and R2 is 3.3MΩ, the gain is 3300000/10000 = 3300 times. Op amps can be wired to have very high gains. But the output can never be more than +V or less than −V. In certain types of op amp, the output voltage is able to swing even less widely. The advantages of op amps are that they are very sensitive and can be wired to produce very high gain, they require very little current at the input side, yet can provide a relatively large current on the output side.

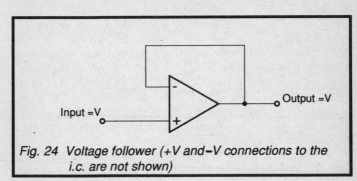

Fig. 24 Voltage follower (+V and−V connections to the i.c. are not shown)

Figure 24 shows an op amp connected as a *voltage follower*. The output voltage exactly equals the input voltage. The point about this circuit is that it takes virtually no input current, as the resistance to current entering the (+) input terminal is usually a million *meg*ohms or more. Yet the output terminal can deliver a relatively large current of many milliamps at the same voltage.

Logic *gates* are the unit circuits that perform simple logical operations. An AND gate (Fig.25a) performs the operation known as AND. Before we can explain what the gate does, we

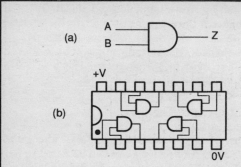

Fig. 25 (a) Symbol for a 2-input AND gate: (b) pin connections of the four AND gates in a 4081 i.c.

need to understand the idea of *logic levels*. In electronic logic systems there are only two states: *true* and *not-true* (= *false*). When we represent facts or statements electronically, so as to handle them in a logical way, we represent a true statement by a high voltage level and a false statement by a low one. At least this is the normal way of doing it, though there are some systems which operate in the reverse way. A high level is taken to be a voltage near to that of the positive supply; a low level is taken to be close to 0V. When writing about logic levels we often represent a high level by the letter 'H' or the figure '1'. Conversely, a low level is represented by 'L' or '0'.

In Figure 25a the two inputs to the gate are labelled A and B; the output is labelled Z. The output of an AND gate is low unless *all* of its inputs are made high. In the case of this gate, Z is high if and only if A AND B are high. Other AND gates may have more than two inputs, and for these Z is high only when A AND B AND C AND . . . are high. With all other combinations of high and low inputs, Z is low. Two-input logic gates have only three terminals so there is room in a 14-pin ic for four such gates, with two pins to spare for the power supply (Fig.25b). Logic gates only ever have one output.

A NOT gate (sometimes called an INVERT gate) has only one input and one output. Its output Z is the opposite of the

34

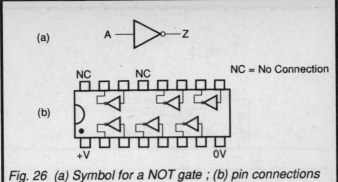

Fig. 26 (a) Symbol for a NOT gate ; (b) pin connections of the six NOT buffer gates in a 4049 i.c.

input A. If A is high, Z is low; if A is low, Z is high. If the input is true the output is NOT true, and the other way about. The symbol for a NOT gate is shown in Figure 26a. There is room in a 14-pin ic for six NOT gates. The 4049 ic used in one of the projects has this arrangement of gates. This particular ic has an additional feature, that each gate is able to supply a larger current at its output than can most types of gate. We call this type of gate a *buffer*. In the case of the 4049, they are *inverting buffers*.

If we take the output from an AND gate and send it directly to a NOT gate (Fig.27a) the action of the combination is the inverse of that of an AND gate, as described above. The output is high *unless* all of the inputs are high. This particular logical result happens to be a very useful one so gates are made which have this action. We call them NAND gates (Fig.27b). The connections of the four 2-input NAND gates in a 4011 ic is the same as in Figure 25b.

It is interesting to see what happens if we join the inputs of a NAND gate together (Fig.28). Either *both* inputs are low or *both* inputs are high. If both are low, the output is high; if both are high, the output is low. In other words, the NAND gate is acting as a NOT gate. This is useful if we need a NOT gate and have a spare NAND gate.

Perhaps the most useful ic ever invented is the 555 timer ic. In this book we use the CMOS version of this, type number

35

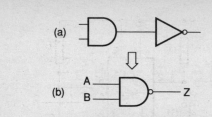

Fig. 27 (a) AND followed by a NOT (b) NAND gate

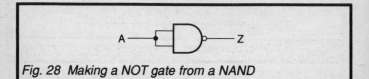

Fig. 28 Making a NOT gate from a NAND

7555, which takes much less current than the original 555 ic. There are many ways of using the timer but they fall into two main headings: (1) to generate a single pulse; (2) to generate an indefinite series of pulses. When it is being used as in (1), we say it is a *monostable*. When used as (2) it is an *astable*.

Figure 29 shows the typical monostable circuit. Note that the line joining IC1 to the output terminal crosses the line between R and C *without* a dot at the crossing. This indicates that these lines are *not connected*. Wherever lines are connected in a circuit, we always draw a large dot on the diagram. The output of the timer at pin 3 is normally 0V. The timer is triggered by pressing S1. When S1 is not pressed, the trigger input at pin 2 is held at +V because of the connection to the +V rail through R1. Pressing S1 reduces the voltage at pin 2, so triggering the ic. Its output immediately rises to +V and stays there for a period *t* seconds, at the end of which it falls instantly to 0V again. The value of *t* can be calculated from:

$$t = 1.1RC$$

where R is in ohms and C is in farads. For example, if $R =$

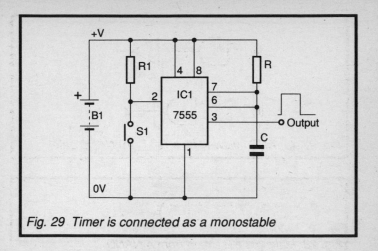

Fig. 29 Timer is connected as a monostable

$22k\Omega$ and $C = 150\mu F$, then:

$$t = 1.1 \times 22000 \times 0.00015 = 3.63s$$

The larger the resistance and the larger the capacitance, the longer the time. Using a resistor (R1) and push-button (S1) to trigger the timer is just one way of doing it; other ways are illustrated in the projects.

The other way of using the timer ic is shown in Figure 30. There is no trigger and the circuit starts to oscillate as soon as the battery is connected. Pin 2 is connected to the positive end of the capacitor, and this causes the ic to be retriggered automatically, so it keeps on running indefinitely. Its output alternates between +V and 0V, producing a series of pulses. The length of time it stays at +V is given by:

$$t_1 = 0.69\,(R_A + R_B)\,C$$

The length of time it stays low is:

$$t_2 = 0.69\,R_B C$$

For example, if $R_A = 100k\Omega$, $R_B = 56k\Omega$, and $C = 220\mu F$,

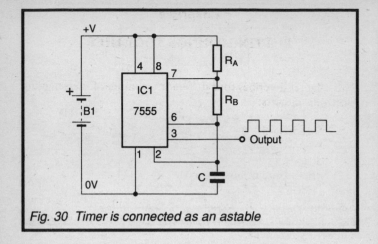

Fig. 30 Timer is connected as an astable

then:

$$t_1 = 0.69 \times 156000 \times 0.00022 = 23.68s$$

$$t_2 = 0.69 \times 56000 \times 0.00022 = 8.50s$$

Combining these equations into one, we calculate the frequency, the number of pulses per second:

$$f = \frac{1.44}{(R_A + 2R_B)C} = \frac{1.44}{(100000 + 112000) \times 0.00022}$$

$$= 0.03087$$

This result is in pulses per second, usually referred to as hertz. The signal is 0.03087Hz. This is a rather low frequency since there is less than one pulse a second. In fact there is one pulse per 1/0.03087s which works out to just over 32s, the total of t_1 and t_2.

38

Chapter 4

PUTTING THINGS TOGETHER

This chapter describes four different techniques for assembling electronic circuits:

1 Breadboard
2 Wire-wrapping
3 Stripboard
4 Printed circuit board (pcb).

Each technique has its advantages and disadvantages. We explain these below so that you can select the technique most suited to your needs.

1 Breadboard

A breadboard (sometimes known as a plugblock) is a plastic base in which are set rows of interconnected metal sockets. Figure 31 shows part of a typical breadboard. The rows are spaced 0.1″ (2.5mm) apart and the sockets are spaced 0.1″

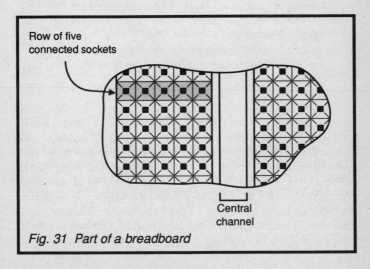

Row of five
connected sockets

Central
channel

Fig. 31 Part of a breadboard

apart in the rows. This makes the board able to accept components with standard pin spacing, for example, ics. The sockets are usually connected in groups of 5, though some boards have longer runs of sockets along the edges. Typically a board has a central channel so that ics can be inserted bridging the channel, without making connections between opposite pins.

Breadboards are used for building temporary circuits. It may be that a project arouses your interest and you want to try it out, without necessarily building it for keeps. You assemble it on the breadboard, which usually takes less than an hour, and it is immediately ready for trials. If you want to experiment with using components of different values, such as resistors and capacitors of lower or higher values than those quoted in the instructions, it is easy and quick to make the necessary changes. In this way you can discover the optimum component values and then, if you wish, build the project in a more permanent form, using one of the other three techniques. Or, if you decide not to go ahead with it, you can remove the components from the breadboard in a few minutes. They and the breadboard are then ready for use in another project.

Summing up, the advantages of breadboarding are:

* speed of assembly
* ability to modify component values and connections
* low cost because components can be re-used
* no soldering.

Figure 32 shows a simple amplifier circuit and Figure 33 shows one way of assembling it on a breadboard. Nine rows of connected sockets are shown; the used sockets are shown blacked in. The wire from battery B1 positive is plugged into the left-hand end of the 1st row of sockets. The wire leads of R1 are bent and inserted in rows 1 and 4. Also in row 4 are the collector lead of T1, and a wire link taking the output of this circuit to another part of the breadboard. R2 joins row 1 and row 5, which also has the base lead of T1 plugged into it. The emitter of T1 is plugged into row 6, which connects it to the wire coming from the 0V side of B1. Capacitor C1 is

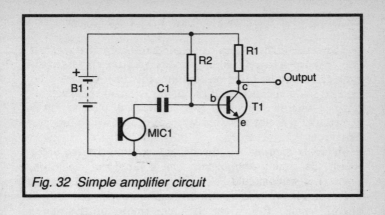

Fig. 32 Simple amplifier circuit

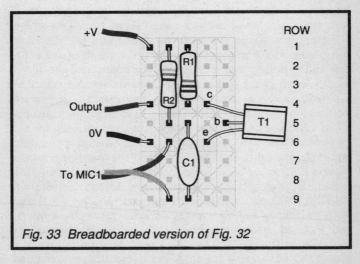

Fig. 33 Breadboarded version of Fig. 32

plugged into row 5 (so that it is connected to one end of R2 and the base of T1) and into row 9. The leads from the microphone MIC1 are plugged into rows 6 (0V) and 9 (C1). It is best if the layout of components on the board follows as closely as possible to the arrangement of the components in the schematic diagram. This makes it easier to trace and check connections. However, there are instances, such as the

41

placing of C1 in this example, where a different arrangement is better.

The main disadvantages of breadboarding are that it is suitable only for relatively simple circuits. All the circuits in this book can easily be fitted on to a breadboard. Another problem that sometimes occurs, if the circuit has many connections, is that a wire or component is accidentally displaced from its socket, and it is not always easy to work out which socket it came from.

Materials required for breadboarding comprise the breadboard, the circuit components, and a supply of connecting wires. The wires should be single-stranded (p.6), and it is best if their insulation is in several different colours. Cut them in lengths ranging from 3cm to 15cm (more of the shorter lengths). Strip about 5mm of insulation from each end of each wire. You also need some wires about 10cm long with a miniature corocodile clip soldered at one end (or with that end of the wire firmly twisted around the shank of the clip). One end is pushed into a socket on the board, and the clip is used to connect the socket to an off-board component such as a potentiometer, a push-button or a loudspeaker. If you are intending to do much breadboarding, it is useful to make up a set of off-board components which you keep specially for the purpose. These have wires soldered to or twisted round their terminals, the other ends being stripped for insertion into the sockets. A set of such components could include: a SPDT switch, a push-button, a loudspeaker, several pots ($1k\Omega$, $10k\Omega$, $100k\Omega$ and $1M\Omega$), a 3.5mm jack socket, a filament lamp holder, an audible warning device, a microphone insert, and a power transistor. Build up your set of components gradually as the needs arise. You may need more than one pot of a given value. It is a good idea to use different coloured wires for the three terminals of pots: red, white (for the wiper) and blue). This makes it easier to trace connections. The same applies to the three terminals of the SPDT switch.

Tools required are minimal. The essential tool is a wire cutter and stripper. You can borrow a soldering iron for making up the optional set of off-board components. It is sometimes useful to have a pair of forceps (tweezers) with blunt tips for inserting wires into sockets, especially when there are several connections to be made on a small area of the board. You may need a small screwdriver for fixing knobs to variable resistors and rotary switches.

2 Wire Wrapping

What we term wire wrapping here is really a simplified version of a technique widely used industrially for assembling electronic equipment. The components are mounted on a rectangle of thick (2mm) cardboard or plastic-board (available from modellers' stores). Holes are drilled in the board to take the terminals wires or pins of the components. The component bodies are all on one side of the board. The wires and pins project through to the other side, and are trimmed with wire cutters so that they project about 3mm from that side of the board. They are joined as required by wrapping fine bare wire around them. Here the technique differs from normal wire-wrapping, which uses insulated wire. If a mistake is made with the connections, or the wrong component is used, it is easy to unwind the wire and correct the error.

The advantages of this wire-wrapping technique are:

* more permanent than breadboarding
* speed of assembly almost as fast as breadboarding
* ability to modify component values and connections easily
* low cost because components can be re-used, and card is cheap
* no soldering

Disadvantages are that the wires sometimes come off (though not often if well wrapped), and that the pins of ics are relatively short and so are tricky to wrap if the card is too thick.

Figure 34 shows how components are wired together in the circuit of Figure 32. In Figure 35 there is a sectional view. The placing of components on the board is optional, the main point being to avoid crossing wires as far as possible. When the layout has been decided upon and a sketch made, mark the board on one side with the positions of the holes for the wires and pins. A stout needle, preferably mounted in a handle, can

43

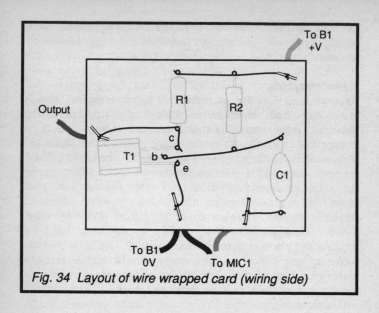

Fig. 34 Layout of wire wrapped card (wiring side)

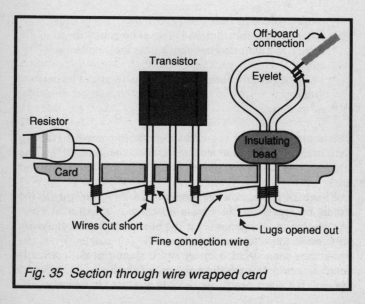

Fig. 35 Section through wire wrapped card

be used for this. The best tool is a modellers' electric drill, with a 1mm bit. Connections to off-board components may be made to a wire staple, inserted from an ordinary desk stapler. Another kind of off-board connector is the gold-plated eyelet shown in Figure 34. The wire should be thin (0.2mm diam) copper or preferably tinned copper. This is not easily available as such (note wire wrapping wire is insulated, so is unsuitable unless you are willing to strip its ends). But a virtually no-cost source of this wire is a discarded length of mains cable. It need be only a few centimetres long. Remove the insulation and separate out the copper strands, there will be around 20 strands in each of the two or three wires, more than enough for any of these projects. Off-board connections are made with multistranded hook-up wire.

Plan the sequence of wiring and the route to be taken by wires that connects several components. As far as possible work in long runs, so that a single wire is twisted round a starting component (or off-board terminal) and goes on to the various components that need to be interconnected, twisted a few turns round each, until all connections have been made. Twisting the wires firmly is the secret of success. One end of the wire is held down firmly against the board. Use a small screwdriver or similar tool for this. The free portion of the wire is held in tweezers (not too finely pointed) and wrapped with about 5 closely-packed spiral turns around the terminal wire or pin. Then the wire is pulled straight across to the next terminal and wrapped around it with about 5 turns. Continue in this way until the last pin is wrapped. Cut off the wire short. Loose ends of wires may cause trouble later by short-circuiting connections; use the tweezers to wrap the loose ends around the starting and finishing terminals.

Inevitably, in all but the simplest of projects, one or more wires need to cross other wires. A small rectangle of PVC insulating tape is used to prevent short-circuiting (Fig.36). Figure 36 also shows insulating tape being used to hold a wire to one side in circumstances in which it might make unwanted contacts if allowed to go straight.

When a circuit has been assembled and tested, it helps to retain the wires in position if the wired side of the board is sprayed with pcb protective lacquer and put aside to dry. It is

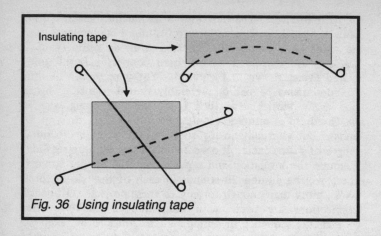

Fig. 36 Using insulating tape

best to apply the lacquer in two or three thin coats, leaving it to dry in between. Take care if there is any insulating tape on the board, for an excess of lacquer may make the tape curl.

Materials required for this wire-wrapping technique are: 2mm card or plastic card, fine wire as described above, hook-up wire, a supply of staples or pcb eyelets, insulating tape, pcb protective lacquer (optional).

Heat-shrink sleeving is another useful material. It is used for strengthening the connections between off-board wires without the need to solder them. Cut a 2cm length of sleeving and thread one of the wires through it. Twist the end of this wire with the end of the wire to be joined to it. Slide the sleeve over the join. Warm the sleeving gently (for example by holding it close to a hot electric lamp). It shrinks to about half its original diameter, firmly gripping and insulating the joint.

Tools required are: mounted needle or drill, tweezers, wire cutters.

3 Stripboard

Stripboard consists of a board made from insulating resin-bonded (SRBP) material. The most useful type is known as *matrix* board and is punched with 1mm holes on a 0.1″ (2.5mm) matrix. Plain matrix boards are available, but the

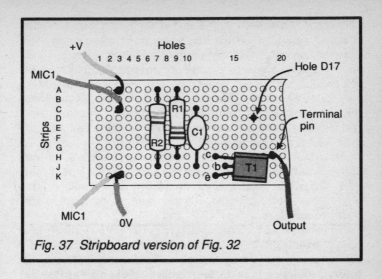

Fig. 37 Stripboard version of Fig. 32

type needed for the projects in this book has parallel strips of copper on one side, running along the rows of holes. There are also boards with different patterns of strips, some specially intended for mounting circuits which have many ics, but all the projects in this book can be assembled on the ordinary matrix board. We have designed the projects so that almost all of them fit on to a board of standard size, 100mm × 25mm, which has 10 strips, each with 39 holes, partly illustrated in Figure 37. Boards of this size are purchased already cut to size. A few of the projects can be built on a smaller board; use a junior hacksaw to trim a standard board to the required size. One project requires a slightly larger board.

Figure 37 also shows the principles of assembling this type of circuit. The components are mounted on the plain side of the board, with their terminal wires passing through the holes and soldered (see below) to the strips on the other side of the board. Connections between components are made by way of the strips. However, unless the circuit is very simple, it is necessary to cut some of the strips so that they can be used for making more than one connection. A special tool, a *spot face cutter*, is used for cutting the strips. A circuit may require wire links to join strips that are not adjacent, or to

47

connect a component at one end of the board with one that is at the other end. Often it is possible to make a connection between adjacent strips by running a blob of molten solder from one strip across to the other. Integrated circuits can be soldered direct to the board but it is preferable to use ic sockets (p.8). For off-board connections, use special 1mm terminal pins that fit firmly into the holes in the board. One end projects from the component side of the board and the other end is soldered to the strip.

Materials for stripboarding comprise the stripboard, terminal pins, components, solder (18swg or 22swg) and connecting wire. It is best to use single stranded wire for links on the board, but multi-stranded flexible wire is better for off-board connections.

Tools required include: spot face cutter (like a drill bit in a plastic handle), wire cutter and stripper, or miniature side cutter (snip cutter), long-nose pliers, heat shunt (optional, see below), soldering iron. A low-wattage (about 15W) soldering iron is preferred and it must have a fine (about 2mm) bit. A soldering iron stand, complete with a sponge for wiping the bit, is almost essential. A magnifier is very useful for examining soldered joints and the cuts in the copper strips.

The project descriptions give full details for assembling on stripboard. Each project has a list telling you exactly where to place each component, where to cut the strips and where to insert wire links. As in Figure 37, we specify the strips by letters A to K (note there is no strip I, to avoid confusion with number 1), from top to bottom as seen from the component side of the board. The holes in a strip are numbered 1 to 39 from left to right. We rarely use holes 1 and 2, or 38 and 39; this leaves the ends of the board clear so that it can fit into the slots in the enclosure (see later). Holes are specified by stating the row letter followered by the hole number (see hole D17 in Fig.37). Remember that when the board is turned over for working on the strip side, with strip A still at the top, the numbering of the holes then runs from right to left.

The first step in assembly is to cut the strips, using the spot face cutter. The project instructions for stripboard layout begin with a list of the required cuts, if any. Working on the strip side of the board, locate a hole at which the strip is to be

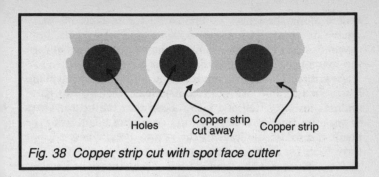

Fig. 38 Copper strip cut with spot face cutter

cut (see note about numbering, above), insert the tip of the cutter into the hole and twist it one way and the other a few times. This completely removes the copper from around the hole so that the strip is cut through (Fig.38). When you have finished all the cuts, inspect all of them using a magnifier; it is easy to leave an almost microscopically fine 'wire' of copper bridging one or both sides of the gap, and this will prevent the circuit from working properly.

Now the board is ready to receive the components. Taking each component in turn, insert it in its holes and solder the wires or pins to the strips. The project instructions list the component locations in the order in which it is usually best to mount the components. In general, we start with links and small components that are mounted close to the board, and continue to the larger components. The way the holes are indicated for each type of component is as follows:

Links: These are wire links between two holes. The instructions show the holes to be joined. For example B14–E14 means a link from hole B14 to E14. Such a link runs straight across the board; strip one end from a coil of wire, insert the bare end in one of the holes and solder it to the copper. Press the wire flat against the board so that it runs across to the other hole. Cut the wire long enough to allow it to be bent and pushed through the hole. Strip the end, insert the bare end and solder it. If the wire is loose on the top of the board, re-melt the solder and use tweezers to pull on the end, making the wire close to the surface of the board. The procedure gives a neat appearance to the project. Some of the links extend along the length of the board, for example B3–H26. These are best left until the other components have been soldered in place, so that they can be routed neatly between the components, *not* pulled tight to the board.

Resistors: The two holes are listed after the resistor number. For example, R2 (C19, G19) means that resistor R2 is inserted in holes C19 and G19. Bend the resistor lead wires so that the ends fit neatly into the two holes. Turn over the board and solder the leads to the strips. Presets have a list of three holes for their terminal pins.

Pins: These are the 1mm terminal pins mentioned earlier. Use single-ended 1mm pins. The instructions list the off-board connection to be made, followed by the hole in brackets. For example +V (A3) indicates a pin in hole A3 for connection to the battery positive, as in Figure 37. Insert the pins from the strip side, pushing them firmly into their holes so that their heads lie flush with the strip. Solder the heads to the strips. A special insertion tool is available, but we have never found this to be helpful.

Capacitors: These are listed in the same way as resistors. With polarised (electrolytic or tantalum) capacitors it is essential to fit the capacitor the right way round. The description lists each terminal separately, for example C2+ (D12), C2– (K12).

Semis: Under this heading we include diodes, transistors and other semiconductor devices. The hole for each terminal is listed separately, for example T1c (D9), T1b (E8), T1e (F9) tells us where to insert the collector, base and emitter leads of a transistor T1. Similarly the anode and cathode of a diode are indicated by a and k respectively. When soldering semiconductors it is advisable to use a heat shunt (see below).

ICs: Using an ic socket is strongly recommended (p.8). The instructions indicate the hole for pin 1 of the ic, which in all projects is socketed so that pin 1 is at the top left corner. Note that, in some cases, one or more copper strips may be left *un*cut beneath the ic to connect pins that are on opposite sides of the ic.

Blobs: These are used to join adjacent strips; instead of using a very short wire link. The holes to be joined are listed, for example F24–G24 (the *numbers* are always the same).

Form a blob of solder beside one of the holes; form a blob beside the other hole. Melt both blobs of solder and add a little more solder to bridge the gap. Sometimes we join three or even more strips by blobs, for example, D25—E35—F25—G25.

Off-board: Under this heading we list the connections to batteries, switches and components not mounted on the stripboard. This wiring is best left until last, when the items to be connected are mounted in the enclosure or on its lid (except where it may be awkward to solder to an inaccessible terminal). Use stranded insulated wire, strip the insulation from the ends. Twist the strands well together so that none stick out sideways. Heat the bare ends and run a *little* solder on to them to make a well-tinned end. Bend this around the terminal (use long-nose pliers), then solder the wire end to the terminal.

Soldering is simple once you have practised it a few times on a spare scrap of stripboard. Start with the iron in its stand or, if you do not have a stand, support it so that the bit is well clear of the workbench and not in contact with anything that could be damaged by heat. Moisten the sponge with water. Plug in the iron, switch it on and leave the iron to warm up for a few minutes. Touch the end of the solder against the hot bit to coat it with molten solder. If there are any black pieces of burned flux on the bit, wipe these off on the sponge.

The essential of good soldering is to bring together the parts to be soldered, heat *both* of them with the bit, apply the end of the solder to *both* of them and let sufficient molten solder run freely between them, so as to coat the joined surfaces. The knack is to have the bit hot enough to heat the surfaces *quickly*, yet not so hot that the component is damaged. If the iron is not hot enough, this may be just as bad as having the iron too hot; it may take so long to heat the surfaces that there is time for heat to be conducted along wires and strips to the body of the component and to other parts of the circuit. As soon as the solder has flowed into the joint, remove the bit. Avoid having too much solder around the joint. Allow the joint to cool for about 10 seconds before moving the wire or component. Then examine the joint; a

51

good joint looks as if the solder is still liquid, flowing smoothly on to and wetting the joined surfaces. A 'dry' joint has an unwetted appearance and is a frequent cause of faulty circuit operation as there is no electrical connection through such a joint.

When soldering diodes, transistors and other semiconductor devices there is a real risk of damaging them if the joint is heated for more than a few seconds. Use a heat shunt to avoid this problem. Clip the shunt on to the terminal wires, then insert the wires through the holes (Fig.37) and solder them in place. Remove the heat shunt immediately.

After a few components have been mounted, the strip side of the board becomes a forest of wire ends. Cut these off as close as possible to the board, using side cutters.

It is normally easy to remove wires and components that have been soldered into the wrong holes. Grip the component or wire with tweezers or long-nose pliers, then use the iron to melt the solder and at the same time pull the wire out of the hole. When removing a semiconductor grip its wires with a heat shunt. Removing a component may leave some of the holes blocked with solder. To clear the hole, grip a short piece of bare single-core wire with tweezers, melt the blocking solder, and poke the wire through the hole a few times until the blockage is cleared.

It is important to check the stripboard after assembly and before testing. Check that:

* all components are present and that polar components (electrolytic capacitors, LEDs, etc.) are mounted the right way round;
* all wire links and solder blobs are in place;
* the strips have been *completely* cut (use a magnifier to inspect);
* there are no fine hairs of solder (or even blobs of solder) joining strips which are not intended to be joined (use a magnifier to inspect for solder hairs).

When the board has passed this inspection, it is ready for testing.

4 Printed Circuit Board

This method has the disadvantage that making the pcb requires more equipment and materials than the other methods, and there are more stages. The big advantage is that, since the pcb already incorporates all the connections required between components, there is much less chance of making mistakes when assembling the circuit. Provided that the soldering is properly done, the circuit should work straight away.

The idea of the method is that we begin with an insulating board (SRBP or fibre-glass) which is coated on one side with copper. Double-sided board is available but is not required for these projects. The copper is to be etched away, using a special chemical but, before doing this, we cover the copper with a *resist* over the areas where the copper is *not* to be etched. These are the circular *pads* to which the components are to be soldered and the *tracks*, or strips of copper which are to make the connections. Resist can take several forms:

* pcb lacquer, applied from a special marker pen; you can also use nail varnish;
* rub-down pcb transfers; sheets of pads, tracks, arrays of pads for ics and other standard outlines are available; apply them to the copper just as you would apply rub-down lettering. Reels of self-adhesive resist are available in several widths for laying down tracks;
* photo-resist, which is explained in more detail below.

Each project description includes two figures for use in pcb assembly. The *component layout* shows how the components are arranged on the pcb. Occasionally there are wire links, which are indicated by straight unlabelled lines. The component layout shows the board as seen from the side on which the components are mounted. The corners of the board are identified by the letters A, B, C, D, with corner A at top left. The *pcb design* is an actual-size pattern showing the pads and tracks. This is shown from the copper side of the board and is therefore the mirror-image of the component layout. The corners are lettered to correspond with the letters shown on the component layout with corner A at top right. Note how the letters themselves are mirror-images of the letters on the component layout.

It is feasible, with the simpler projects at least, to use a resist pen or rub-down transfers. First the copper side of the board must be cleaned to remove all traces of grease. Special polishing blocks are available but a domestic scouring compound (for example, Jif) is suitable. Rinse the board thoroughly after cleaning, taking care to handle it only by its edges, and leave it propped up to drain and dry. Copy the design from the book on to the copper, using the marker pen or transfers, or a combination of both. Take care not to touch the surface of the board with your fingers while doing this. When the design is finished, check it very carefully, as it is difficult to correct errors once the board has been etched. It is then ready for etching, as described later.

The photo-resist method is quicker and error-free but requires more materials and equipment than the other methods. The first step is to obtain a positive transparency of the pcb design. This can be done on an ordinary photocopier; ask the operator to make the photocopy on to transparent film and to set the copier to make a dark copy. The copy must be made actual size. With most copiers this will produce a suitable transparency on standard film, but a better copy may be made using a special film known as Letracopy. This is available from the larger stationers and other vendors of Letraset products (see appendix).

In the photo-resist method we use a board which has a photosensitive layer over the copper. If you are coating your own board, this must first be cut to size with a junior hacksaw, its edges smoothed with a file, and then cleaned, as described above. It is then sprayed with photo-resist, under low light conditions. Follow the instructions on the spray can. Leave the coated board in a dark place to dry. Ready-coated board is usually supplied with its sensitive surface protected by a black plastic film. Cut the board to size and smooth the edges before peeling off the black film. Return the unused part of the board, with its black film still intact, to the packet.

The next step is to make a 'contact print' of the transparency on to the sensitive surface of the coated board, using ultra-violet light. If you have a UV exposure unit, place the transparency on the glass, checking that it is the right way round to produce a design that matches the design in the project description. Place the board, sensitive side down, on top of it. Close the unit and switch on for the prescribed length of time, as quoted in the instruction book supplied with the unit. Unfortunately, UV exposure units are expensive. If you have only a few small pcbs to make, you may be able to borrow one. If not, make use of a natural source of UV — the sun. Even if the sky is cloudy, UV penetrates the clouds, so there is no need to wait for a sunny day. You need a printing frame, which is a device to hold the transparency flat against the coated board. It is quite easy to rig up something of this kind using a sheet of glass and a rectangle of hardboard, plus some stout elastic bands. A photographic shop may be able to supply you with a ready-made printing frame. Place the board in the frame with the transparency against it. Place the frame outdoors, away from the shade of buildings and trees. Tilt it so that the sunlight falls perpendicularly on it (or would if there were no clouds). An exposure time of approximately 10 minutes is usually sufficient for exposures during the period from mid-morning to mid-afternoon.

If you are in doubt about exposure time, try a test strip. Cut a piece of sensitised board about 1cm × 10cm. Place this in the frame behind the transparency. Close the frame, then lay a piece of black card on the frame so that it shades about two-thirds of the strip from the light. Expose the frame for 10 minutes, then move the card along to cover only one-third of the strip and expose again for 5 minutes more. Finally, remove the card altogether and expose the frame for another 5 minutes. This will give you a test strip exposed for 5, 10 and 20 minutes. When this is developed (see below), you will be able to judge the best exposure length.

The board can be processed in a glass dish or a plastic dish sold specially for the purpose. Use plastic forceps or tweezers to handle the board — do not use your fingers. Agitate the board continually. An alternative method is to use the range of solutions packed in sponge-tipped dispensers (similar to those used for certain brands of shoe-polish). The range includes photo-resist developer, etchant and photo-resist remover. The board is placed on a sheet of plastic or glass and the appropriate solution is squeezed on to the board from the dispenser. The sponge tip is wiped over the surface of the board repeatedly until the processing stage is complete. Holding it by the edges, the board is then rinsed under a running cold tap. Using these packs is slightly more expensive than dish processing, but they are much easier and safer to handle. They are ideal for processing the small boards in this book.

Various pcb photo-resist developers are available for dish processing. Follow the instructions on the bottle or dispenser working under dim indoor light. The image of the pcb design develops as a blue or green design on a clear (copper) background. As it develops, watch carefully to see that the details of the finest tracks have appeared. Rinse the board, ready for etching.

The etching process is common to all pcb techniques. The least troublesome method is to use the chemical dispenser mentioned above. It is also possible to obtain etching kits in which the ferric chloride solution is contained in a stout plastic bag. The board is placed directly in the bag and etched there. Follow the instructions in the handbook supplied with the kit.

For dish processing, make up and use a solution of ferric chloride according to the instructions on the bottle or packet. Take care with etchant as it is a corrosive solution. Keep it away from the skin, eyes, clothing and furniture. Ferric chloride stains badly. In case of accidents, flood the affected areas or objects liberally with water. These remarks apply also to accidents with the plastic bag method.

Etching usually begins near the edges of the board, but wait until the whole board is etched. Large areas of copper (pinky-red while etching) may take much longer than other areas to etch away. Check that narrow zones between closely-placed tracks clear completely, otherwise you will have trouble with short-circuits later. When etching is complete, rinse and dry the board. Remove the resist. Lacquer may be removed with special etch resist remover. Transfers are removed by abrasive. Photo-resist is removed by dilute sodium hydroxide solution, which is more safely used from a dispenser. When the resist is gone, and the copper tracks and pads are visible, polish the copper with fine abrasive, rinse the board and wipe it dry with a clean paper tissue.

The final stage in pcb production is drilling the holes for the terminal wires and pins. For most of the holes including the holes for terminal pins, use a 1mm drill bit. Usually the pcb pads (including the ones in this book) have a clear dot in the centre. This results in the pad being etched away in the very centre, leaving a depression which helps to locate the drill bit exactly in the centre of the pad. A miniature electric drill, operating on a 12V (or lower) DC supply, is ideal for this purpose. Take special care with the spacing of holes when drilling for an ic socket. A bit of larger diameter (1.5mm) may be needed for components with larger terminals, such as presets and power transistors.

Once the board is finished, the components are mounted according to the component layout diagram. The technique of mounting and soldering is the same as that for mounting on stripboard (pages 49—52), except that very few wire links are needed and pcb designs do not require solder blobs.

Enclosures

Most projects benefit from being housed in a proper box. The most inexpensive enclosures are those modelled from ABS plastic, available in a range of sizes and shapes. They are usually black, grey or white. Most types have ridges on the insides of the walls, making slots for holding stripboards or pcbs. For preference, choose a box of a size to fit the stripboard or pcb of your project. Most of the projects use a standard stripboard 100mm long, so for these select a box which has one of its *internal* dimensions of this size. The enclosure must also be large enough to hold the battery or battery-box and any other off-board components, as discussed in the *Planning* section of each project.

An alternative method of fixing small circuit boards is to use a lump of Blu-Tack, or one or two of the double-sided adhesive pads sold under the name 'Sticky Fixer'. These can also be used for securing battery holders in position. Enclosures can be obtained with built-in battery compartments and you could consider using one of these for certain projects.

The off-board components such as LEDs, switches, terminal posts, and potentiometers are mounted on the plastic lid of the box or on a special aluminium panel if one of the better quality enclosures is used. The instructions list the items for panel mounting, and it is important to plan the layout before drilling the panel. The layout should take into account such aspects as the size of the component and any operating knobs, the logical arrangement of controls for convenience in use, and the positioning of displays for clear visibility. Also remember that, when the panel or lid is finally in position, anything mounted on it may touch against the circuit board or one of the large components on it (such as transistors, relays, electrolytic capacitors), or against items mounted on the wall of the enclosure, such as a loudspeaker or switch.

When a satisfactory and pleasing layout has been decided upon, mark the positions of the centre of each hole on the rear of the lid or panel, using a sharp-pointed scriber (point of a pair of compasses). You need a hand-drill or power-drill with a few twist bits ranging in diameter from 2mm up to 8mm. You also need one or two circular files or a reamer for enlarging holes to non-standard sizes. LEDs can be mounted by drilling a hole of the appropriate diameter and inserting the LED directly in this. A neater method is to use a plastic LED clip. Pots and rotary switches often need a hole 10.5mm or more in diameter. The best way of cutting this is to use a chassis punch (sheet metal punch) of the appropriate diameter, but these are expensive. If you need a large-diameter hole only occasionally, it is practicable with a plastic lid or panel to drill as large a hole as possible (say 8mm) with an ordinary drill and enlarge it with a reamer or circular file.

When all the holes are drilled, mount the components in them. Then complete the off-board wiring. Often the power lines (+V and 0V) can be taken from component to component on the panel, with just *one* wire going to the circuit board. The wires between the panel and the circuit board should be long enough to allow for the enclosure to be opened and the circuit board pulled slightly out for testing, but not so long that the interior of the enclosure is stuffed with a jumble of wires when the panel is fixed in position.

When all the connections to the circuit-board have been made and you are closing the box, look carefully to make sure that this does not bring any metal part of the panel-mounted components into contact with metal parts of board-mounted components. A short-circuit could prevent the circuit from functioning properly.

Chapter 5

TROUBLE SHOOTING

Most projects work the first time the power is switched on, but occasionally a project may fail. This is when you need to refer to this chapter. Each of the projects gives you testing routines specific to that project. In this chapter we look at some techniques applicable to practically all circuits. We can divide the techniques into two kinds:

1 Those done before applying power to the circuit (or after switching it off hastily in response to a smell of hot plastic!)

2 Those done with power applied.

Before we describe the tests, we discuss the most frequently used testing instrument, the multimeter. Although it is possible to manage without one of these with simple circuits, sooner or later a multimeter becomes essential. A multimeter is so-called because it measures voltage, current, resistance and possibly capacitance and frequency as well. Many have a built-in continuity checker and a transistor tester. Although you may not need these additional facilities at first, they will be useful should your interest in electronics grow. There is a bewildering array of models to choose from at a wide range of prices. Buy the best model that you can reasonably afford. The main choice lies between those with a moving-coil meter and those with a digital display. Some people prefer the moving-coil type because it is easier to watch the needle moving smoothly over the scale than to read a four-digit display with continually changing digits. Other people prefer the digital type because of its 4-figure readout, although there is rarely the need to work to this degree of precision. Some of the more expensive digital meters also have a bar-scale which functions in place of a moving needle, so combining the best features of both kinds of multimeter. Reading resistance values is generally more difficult on the moving-coil meters as the graduations on the resistance scale are more crowded toward one end. Some models of digital multimeter feature low-voltage resistance measuring; this makes it possible to check resistances without removing ics or semiconductor devices from the circuit.

The meter of a moving-coil multimeter is connected to the probes through a resistor network. The dial is marked with its sensitivity. In the cheapest models the sensitivity is $2k\Omega/V$. This means that the resistance of the meter on the 2.5V range is $5k\Omega/V$; on the 10V range it is $20k\Omega$. Such a meter draws an appreciable current from the circuit under test. If currents in the circuit are small, this results in an inaccurate reading. The sensitivity of the more expensive moving-coil meters is in the region of $20k\Omega/V$, reducing inaccuracies accordingly. The sensitivity of digital meters is higher still, usually several megohms, because the input goes to a field effect transistor.

1 Tests with Power Off

These tests are mainly a matter of checking that points in the circuit that should be electrically connected are in fact connected. Also that points that are not supposed to be connected are not in fact connected. In other words, we are looking for open circuits and short circuits.

Before starting any tests, check the circuit board and off-board wiring visually to see that all the components and wire links are there and in their correct places. Check that polarised components are inserted the right way round. Check that every ic is inserted in its socket the right way round and that each pin really goes into the socket, and is not bent inward, under the ic.

Check solder joints. If any look suspiciously like a dry joint (p.52), remake the joint by heating it with the soldering iron and applying a little more solder.

Use a magnifier when checking for short circuits such as: stripboard strips not cut properly; pcb tracks and pads not sufficiently etched to leave a clear gap between adjacent tracks and pads; blobs or hairs of solder in the wrong places.

A continuity tester is invaluable for checking out the connections of a circuit. It is handy for identifying dry joints. Continuity testers are cheap to buy, but many models of multimeter have one built in. Failing this, wire a low-voltage battery in series with a filament lamp, an LED, or an electronic buzzer, as in Figure 39. The two probes are touched against the points in the circuit which are supposed to be (or not to be) connected. If they are connected, the lamp comes on or the buzzer sounds; if they are not, nothing happens.

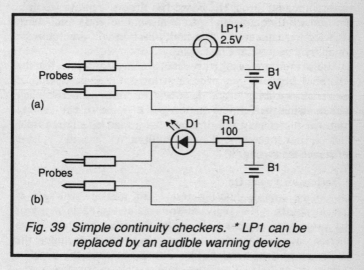

Fig. 39 Simple continuity checkers. * LP1 can be replaced by an audible warning device

Using a continuity tester, try these tests to begin with:

1 Probes to a +V pin and a 0V pin; should be no connection.
2 One probe on a +V pin and one to the leads or terminals of any component that is supposed to be directly connected to +V. Should be a connection in every case.
3 One probe on a 0V pin and one to the leads or terminals of any component that is supposed to be directly connected to 0V. Should be a connection in every case.

It is usually fairly easy to locate the site of an open circuit. Given a series of points which, according to the circuit diagram, are supposed to be joined, place one probe at one end of the series. Work along the series with the other probe until you come to the point where an open-circuit is first indicated. The open circuit must be between that point and the one previously checked. It is sometimes difficult to locate the exact site of a short-circuit, particularly if it is a short between +V and 0V. Visual inspection may help; look in particular for signs of overheating. Failing this the only course is to isolate portions of the circuit by removing one or two components from the board (no need to remove resistors or capacitors completely; just remove one end) and check each section separately. The faulty section will eventually be found by a process of elimination.

Use a multimeter on its resistance range to check that the resistance between two pads or strips is the same as that of the resistors joining them. It is best to remove ics from their sockets while performing these tests as some of the current from the meter may pass through the ics, giving a false result. This is not necessary if your multimeter has low-voltage resistance measuring.

2 Tests with Power On

The main trouble-shooting test is to measure voltages at critical points. The expected voltages are listed in many of the project descriptions. For the following general voltage checks, switch the meter to a range which includes the maximum voltage level (V+). Touch (or clip) the negative (black) probe to a 0V terminal pin, switch on the power, and use the positive (red) probe to monitor these voltages:

1 The positive terminal of the battery and all terminals and pins that are directly connected to the +V line; all should read the same, the full battery voltage. If the voltage is a volt or two lower, suspect an exhausted battery. If the voltage is very low or zero, suspect a short-circuit between the V+ and 0V rails (see test 1, section 1 above); if the voltage is not the same at all points, there is probably a break in the +V line.

2 The negative terminal of the battery and all terminals and pins that are directly connected to the 0V line; if any point is not at 0V, this may indicate an open-circuit on the 0V line.

3   The base terminals of transistors; should be 0.6V or more, unless the circuit allows the transistor to be switched fully off. If the base is less than 0.6V (off) the collector terminal of that transistor should generally be close to +V. If the base is more than 0.6V (on) the collector terminal should be appreciably less than +V, perhaps half that value. In most circuits the emitter is connected directly to 0V so should be at 0V. If these readings are not found, suspect a faulty transistor.

4   With CMOS ics, outputs should normally be either high (close to +V) or low (close to 0V). In-between output voltages may means that the output is alternating between low and high too rapidly for the meter to follow. If an output is not supposed to be alternating rapidly and you still get an in-between reading, it may mean that one of the connections to the ic is wrong − not necessarily the one showing the in-between readings. Quite often this fault is found when the +V or the 0V connection is open-circuit and current is entering or leaving the ic through one or more of the other connections. Remove the ic from its socket and check for open circuits; also that none of the pins are bent.

5   If an LED fails to light when it should do, the most frequent fault is that it is connected the wrong way round. Some makes of LED have the 'flat' on the anode side, so turn the LED round and try again. If it still does not light, it may be burnt out. LEDs can be checked on the diode checker of a multimeter. Usually LEDs can be checked without removing them from the board. Test the voltage at both terminals. In a properly working (lit) LED, the anode is about 1V higher than the cathode. In a faulty (not lit) LED both terminals may be at the same voltage (LED is a short-circuit) or their voltages may differ by more than 1 or 2V (LED is an open-circuit). In either case, replace the LED.

Part B

PROJECTS TO BUILD

Chapter 6

TEN FIRST PROJECTS

In this chapter we present a selection of projects suitable for when you first try your hand at electronics construction. The projects are all based on just one active device — transistor or integrated circuit — and sometimes a light-emitting diode. The circuits are specially designed to need no complicated setting up. But, just because they are simple, this does not mean that there is nothing in this chapter to interest the more experienced constructor. Several of the projects have useful applications around the home. There are also circuits that illustrate ways of using some very ingenious ics. Browse through this chapter and choose any one that arouses your interest. Refer back to the first part of the book (particularly (pp.3—26 and 39—59) for detailed information on components and techniques.

Project 1 — Moisture Detector
An electric tumble-drier may be a useful domestic aid, but there is nothing to beat a good 'blow in the sunshine' for drying the weekly wash. The problem is that sunny days may soon turn to showers and the washing is made wetter than ever. This project detects the first scattered raindrops, warning you to bring in the clothes before they become saturated.

It has other applications too, notably as a water-level detector to warn when a tank is on the brink of overflowing.

The circuit is built around a unijunction transistor (T1, Fig.40). When there is an electrical path from one probe terminal to another, current flows through the probe, through R1 and gradually charges C1. The rising voltage on C1 eventually reaches a level at which the capacitor is rapidly discharged through the emitter of T1. A large current passes from emitter to base-1. With the values of R1 and C1 given in the diagram, charging and discharging is repeated several hundreds or thousands of times a second. The result is a pulsing current through LS1, producing an audible sound.

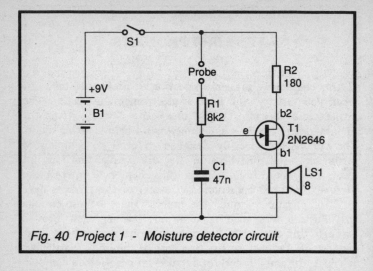

Fig. 40 Project 1 - Moisture detector circuit

Component notes: T1 is made in two different cases, one metal and the other plastic (see Fig.15, p.19). Either type is suitable.

Planning: The circuit requires 2mA continuously, more when it is sounding. It produces a louder sound when run on 9V, but is reasonably loud with a 6V supply. A PP3 battery is conveniently small and lasts for about 10 days. For longer periods use a battery of 4 or 6 larger cells. The enclosure needs space for the speaker; this can be a miniature speaker (38mm diam). If an 8Ω speaker is not available, try using one of higher resistance, such as 64Ω.

For a rain detector, the probe is a piece of stripboard connected as in Figure 41. The larger the board, the more likely it is to detect the first few drops of rain. For sensing water level, use two pieces of stout copper wire about 5cm long pushed through a block of plastic or wood.

Stripboard layout:
Size: Standard
Resistors: R1 (C19, G19), R2 (A26, E26).
Pins: +V (A15), 0V (K15), probe (A17, C15), speaker (J15).

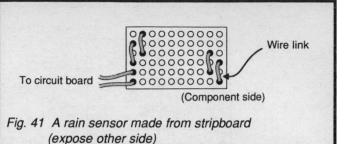

Fig. 41 A rain sensor made from stripboard
(expose other side)

Capacitors: C1 (G16–K20).
Semis: $T1b_2$ (E23), T1e (G23), $T1b_1$ (J26).
Off-board: The cables connecting the probe and the speaker to the board may be several metres long, if necessary.

Panel mounting: Provide for the speaker, and for the on-off switch. Sockets may be needed for the probe and speaker cables, if any. But connections may be made directly to the board, if preferred.

Testing: The voltage at the emitter of T1 must be between about 2V and 3.5V for the oscillator to operate. A voltage lower than this usually means that the total resistance of probe and R1 is too low. PCB assembly details are shown in Figures 42 and 43.

Project 2 — Transistor Tester
This project is for testing npn bipolar junction transistors — the sort you are likely to be using far more than any other sort. It does not tell you if the transistor is up to its full specification but tells quite clearly whether or not it is still capable of functioning as a transistor. The circuit works with all kinds of npn transistors, including power transistors and radio-frequency types.

The circuit (Fig.44) is a 2-transistor oscillator in which the transistor to be tested takes the role of one of the transistors. The oscillator runs at about 7Hz, flashing an LED as it does so.

71

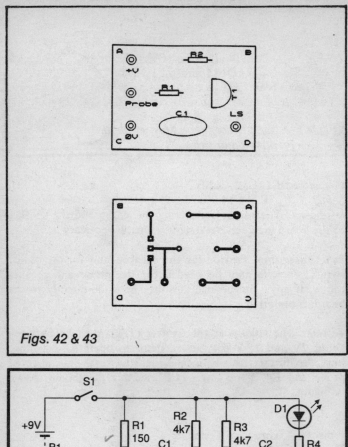

Figs. 42 & 43

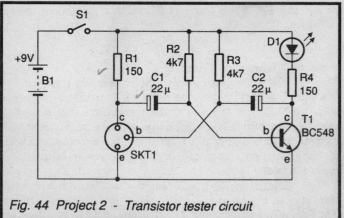

Fig. 44 Project 2 - Transistor tester circuit

If the LED is flashing, we can be sure that the test transistor is operative.

Component notes: It is suggested that a high-intensity LED is used for D1, though one of ordinary power may be used. SKT1 is a 3-pin TO18 transistor socket.

Planning: Probably you will decide that this can be left as a bare-board project, since all components are mounted on the board, with the possible exception of S1. This is not strictly necessary; the project can be 'switched on' simply by pushing the battery connector on to the battery.

Stripboard layout:
Size: Standard.
Cuts: C28.
Links: G6–K6, B14–E14, F20–J20, C26–G26.
Resistors: R1 (A6–E6), R2 (A18–H18), R3 (A22–J22), R4 (C30–G30).
Pins: +V (A3), 0V (K3).
Capacitors: C1+ (B16), C1– (H16), C2+ (C24), C2– (J24).
Sockets: SKT1c (E10), SKT1b (F11), SKT1e (G10). Mark the individual sockets c, b and e.
Semis: D1a (A34), D1k (C34), T1c (G28), T1b (H28), T1e (K28).

Testing: Insert a test transistor in SKT1, taking care that the pins are inserted correctly. If the LED does not flash, check that it is the right way round. If the LED still does not flash, check all wiring and soldered joints. As a final remedy, change the test transistor, also try changing T1. PCB assembly details are shown in Figures 45 and 46.

Project 3 – Remote-reading Thermometer
Being able to measure temperature at a distance can be useful. You can discover the temperature in the greenhouse, wine-brewing cupboard, garage, nursery, or loft, without having to visit these places. The precision of this thermometer is not high, but is adequate for many purposes.

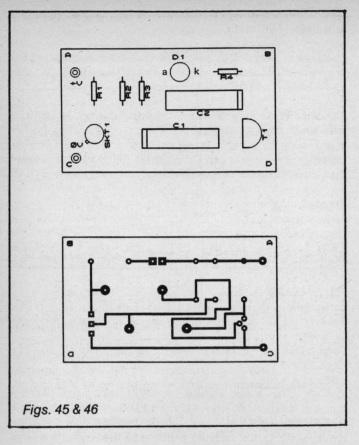

Figs. 45 & 46

The circuit is a unijunction oscillator (see Project 1) and its action is based on the fact that when the current flowing to the capacitor (C1, Fig.47) is equal to the current flowing through the UJT at each discharge, the circuit ceases to oscillate. Oscillations are made visible by passing the current through an LED which flashes. If the total resistance of the thermistor TH1 and the two variable resistors VR1 and VR2 is less than a certain amount, oscillation ceases and the LED glows steadily. The point at which oscillation ceases is sharply defined, and we use this as the end-point of reference for

74

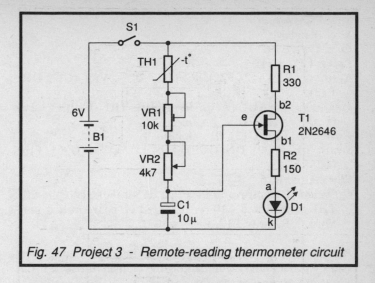

Fig. 47 Project 3 - Remote-reading thermometer circuit

measuring temperature. As temperature falls and the resistance of TH1 increases, we have to decrease the resistance of VR2 to make the same total resistance (assuming we do not alter VR1). The position to which VR2 is turned is a measure of the temperature of TH1. We calibrate a scale around the knob of VR2 to read temperatures directly. VR1 is used for setting the minimum temperature we wish to be able to read.

Component notes: TH1 is a disc thermistor with a resistance of 500Ω at $25°C$. VR1 is an ordinary miniature horizontal trimpot. VR2 can be an ordinary potentiometer but since it is important to have a really linear track (so equal amounts of turn give equal changes of resistance) and since a hard-wearing track is preferable, it is better for VR2 to be a conductive plastic or Cermet type. D1 is preferably a high-intensity LED.

Planning: The circuit occupies only the central part of the standard stripboard, so there is the possibility of using a smaller enclosure than usual.

75

Stripboard layout:
Size: Standard.
Cuts: D19, E19.
Links: F31—K31.
Resistors: R1 (A22—E22), R2 (D27—J27), VR1 (C13, D16, E13).
Pins: +V and TH1 (A10), 0V (K10), TH1 (C10), VR2aw (E10), VR2b (G10).
Capacitors: C1+ (G13), C1— (K22).
Semis: D1a (D29), D1k (F29), T1b$_1$ (J25), T1e (G25), T1b$_2$ (E25).
Blobs: C16—D16.
Off-board: B1 positive to S1; other terminal of S1 to pin A10. TH1 to A10 and C10 (or mounted on board in that position). VR2aw to E10; VR2b to G10.

Panel mounting: S1, VR2 (needs a pointer knob and a clear area of panel round it for marking the temperature scale). Cut a hole in the panel so that D1 is visible.

Testing: Turn VR1 and VR2 right, to their maximum setting. Apply power. D1 flashes about 5 times a second; actually, the LED is on all the time and the flashes are brief increases of brightness. Turning either VR1 or VR2 to the left increases the rate of flashing slightly until, at the end-point, the LED shines brightly without flashing. If the LED does not light, check that it is mounted the correct way round. Also check the voltages at the terminals of T1 which are 1.8V at b_1, 3.7—5.7V at e (depending on the setting of VR1 and VR2) and 5.7V at b_2.

Calibrating: Use another thermometer for calibrating and be sure to leave this and the thermistor for several minutes at each temperature to give them a chance to settle. Decide on which temperature is to be the least that the thermometer will read. You might decide on 0°C, in which case, place some ice cubes in a glass of water for a minute or two, then put the thermistor into the water (you do not need the other thermometer for this). Turn VR2 fully left and mark the position of the pointer on the scale. Adjust VR1 until the LED *just* ceases

to flash. VR1 is not altered after this. Now place the thermistor and thermometer in beakers of water at a series of
temperatures in the range that you wish to cover. At each
temperature, turn VR2 until flashing just ceases and mark
the position of the pointer. It is convenient if you can calibrate in steps of exactly 5° or 10° but, if not, mark the scale
temporarily and later work out where the even 5's or 10's
should be. The points are crowded together toward the top
end of the scale but usually this is no problem as this is above
the range of interest.

PCB assembly details are shown in Figures 48 and 49.

Project 4 – Glittering Party-wear

Artistic creativity and skill with your hands play a large part
in making this project effective. The idea is to decorate a
ready-made or specially-made pendant, ear-rings, brooch or
belt, with one or more flashing LEDs. Make the mount from
pottery, fired and painted with bright glazes, or from leather,
wood, plastics, stainless steel, or any other suitable material.
Or, for a funny effect, buy or make an extravagant party-hat
and scatter flashing LEDs of various colours across it.

The circuit is simplicity itself. It consists of one or more
flashing LEDs wired in parallel (Fig.50) and powered by a 6V
battery. These LEDs each have an integrated circuit inside
them to make them flash about once a second. When power
is applied they all flash at slightly different rates, and out of
step with each other, creating a pleasantly scintillating effect.

Component notes: The LEDs must be of the flashing type
which operate on 6V and do not require a resistor in series
with them.

Planning: Designing the mount is a matter of artistic ability
and skills at working with the chosen materials. Decide how
many LEDs there are to be and where they are to be placed.
Flashing LEDs are available in red, yellow, or green, so a

77

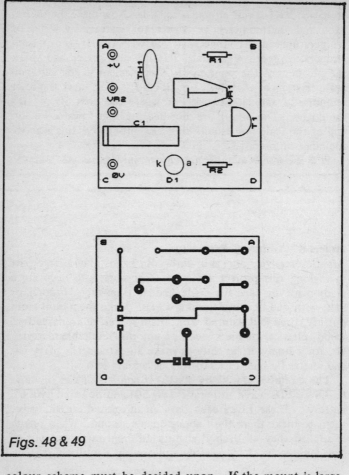

Figs. 48 & 49

colour scheme must be decided upon. If the mount is large enough, the battery consists of four type AA or AAA cells in a battery box. It can be hidden behind a belt, for example; it might be possible to make a small pocket on the inside of the belt to hold the battery. Similarly, it is easy to conceal the battery inside a hat. With a brooch, it is usually possible to run a thin lead down to a battery box hidden in a dress or jacket pocket. With small items such as pendants and ear-

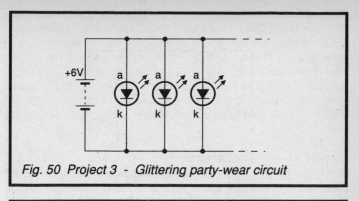

Fig. 50 Project 3 - Glittering party-wear circuit

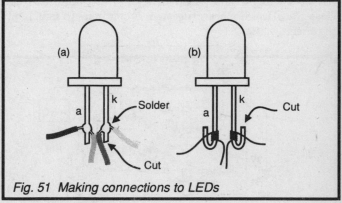

Fig. 51 Making connections to LEDs

rings, concealing the battery is more of a problem. One way out is to make up a battery of four button cells or to use a 6V silver oxide battery (for example, type 4SG13) as used in photographic equipment. This is fastened to the rear of the mount. Small batteries tend to be expensive and to go flat after an hour or two of use. They are not recommended if more than 4 LEDs are to be powered.

Construction: Make holes in the mount or in other ways secure the LEDs in place. Take care to avoid short-circuits with metal mounts. Join all the anodes together, and all the cathodes together. It is preferable to solder the connecting wires about one-third of the way along the LED leads, then cut the leads short (Fig.51a). Take care not to overheat the LEDs whilst doing this. Work quickly, and if possible use a heat shunt. If you use thin connecting wire (strip the insulation from some stranded wire and use the separate strands), a reasonably reliable connection may be made by simply wrapping the connecting wire around the lead. Cut the lead short, bend it over and squeeze it tightly with pliers (Fig.51b).

Project 5 – Intruder Detector
The detector sounds an alarm when the intruder passes between the detector and a source of light. The light source can be a window in daylight or a lamp or fluorescent tube. Once the alarm has been triggered, it continues to sound until the circuit is reset.

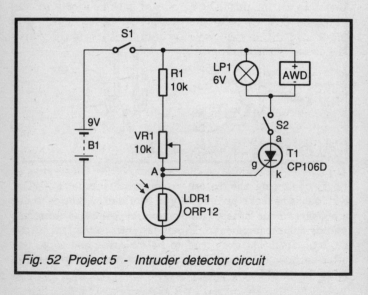

Fig. 52 Project 5 - Intruder detector circuit

The detector is set up on one side of a room or corridor, with the light source on the other side. Switch S2 is closed. The sensor is a light-dependent resistor (LDR1, Fig.52). Its resistance increases when the amount of light reaching it is reduced. This causes a rise in voltage at A, which triggers the thyristor, making it conduct. The lamp comes on and the AWD or siren sounds. The only way to reset the circuit is to open S2.

Component notes: The LDR specified is an ORP12, but there are many other types which work just as well. Some have greater or lesser resistance than an ORP12 at a given light level, in which case it may be necessary to change the value of R1. S2 can be a push-to-break push-button or a switch.

Planning: The circuit can be built with all components, including the AWD and LDR enclosed in one small box. It takes only 0.5mA, so can run on a PP3 battery. However, you may prefer to mount the LDR externally, making it easy to conceal, and connect it to the rest of the circuit which is in another room. In that way, the intruder is less likely to spot the device and switch it off.

Stripboard layout:
Size: Standard.
Resistors: R1 (A16, E16), LDR (G20, K20).
Pins: +V (A13), 0V (K13), VR1a (E13), VR1wb (G13), LP1 (A22), AWD+ (A24).
Semis: T1a (F24), T1g (G24), T1k (K24).
Off-board: B1 positive to one terminal of S1; B1 negative to 0V. S2 to pin F26, other terminal to LP1 and AWD—. There is space for mounting LP1 (in a socket) and the AWD on the board. LDR1 can be off-board, in which event solder its leads to pins at G20 and K20.

Panel mounting: Space required for S1, S2, VR1. If LDR1 is on the board, cut a hole in the case so that light can pass in and fall directly on the LDR. Orientate the LDR so that its face is perpendicular to the incident light. If LP1 is on the board, cut a hole in the case so that it is visible. If the AWD is not on the board, mount it on the case or, if it is too large, externally.

Testing: With the LDR exposed to ordinary room lighting or diffused daylight, adjust VR1 until the voltage at point A (pin G13) is just less than 0.6V. Shading the LDR makes LP1 and the AWD come on. Opening S2 turns them off and, provided the LDR is not shaded, closing S2 again does not make them come on. If the circuit does not behave as described, adjust VR1.

PCB assembly details are shown in Figures 53 and 54.

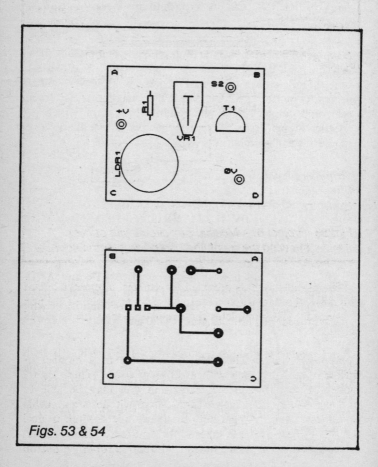

Figs. 53 & 54

Project 6 – Musical Box

Any small box such as a trinket box, a sewing box or a tea caddy can be given extra interest by having this music generator installed. When the lid is opened the melody sounds just once. The idea can be extended to a musical toy cupboard, or you can fix it to the front door to welcome visitors with a pleasant tune.

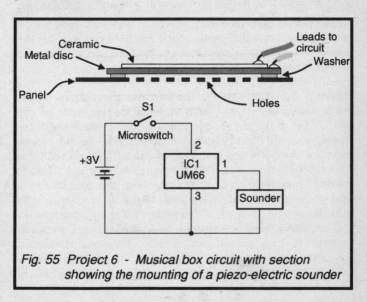

Fig. 55 Project 6 - Musical box circuit with section showing the mounting of a piezo-electric sounder

The 64-note tune is provided by a special integrated circuit (Fig.55). A microswitch is set to close when the lid of the box is opened. This completes the circuit and the tune is played through.

Component notes: The UM66 is available in a number of different versions, each with a different tune. These ics are made for musical greetings cards and you may be able to obtain a free ic from such a card. Microswitches are available in various forms. A light-duty miniature microswitch is ideal for this project as the ic takes so little current. Microswitches are actuated either with a button, a lever or a roller. A button or lever is likely to be most suitable. The sounder can be a piezo-electric transducer. These are good where space is limited (they are often used in watches and clocks, where the enclosure is shallow). But mounting them requires care and a much pleasanter sound is obtained by using a dynamic microphone as a sounder. A dynamic microphone insert with impedance in the order of 250Ω to 500Ω gives a loud, rich sound. This is the kind of microphone often provided with budget-priced tape recorders; maybe you already have such a microphone, no longer used, which can be taken over for this project. A crystal microphone can be used as a sounder but volume tends to be low and quality poor.

Planning: Consider where in the box you are going to mount the microswitch. Usually it is mounted on the inside of one side of the box, just below the top edge. When the lid is closed, a small block of plastic fixed inside the lid presses down on the lever and turns the switch off. When the lid is opened, the spring action of the switch turns it on. Usually a switch operated by a lever is better than one operated by a button as only a small movement of the lid is necessary to turn the switch on or off. The circuit takes no current when it is not operating and less than 1mA when playing, so it can be powered by a pair of button cells. These and the circuit are easily concealed somewhere in the box, perhaps under a false bottom. If space is not a premium, use a 2-cell battery box for type AA or AAA cells.

Construction: No circuit board is needed. Join the components with short lengths of stranded wire, taking care to avoid short-circuits. Heat-shrink sleeving (p.46) helps to make the joints stronger. Secure the ic to the battery box or to the sounder by wrapping insulating tape around both.

If you are inexperienced with soldering, it is safer to buy a transistor socket and solder the wires to that, *then* insert the ic in the socket. This makes it easy to remove the ic, if necessary, while testing the circuit, and also to replace the ic with another of the same kind but playing a different tune.

If you are using a piezo-electric sounder, this must be mounted on a firm panel of thick card, plasticard or plastic.

The bigger and stiffer the panel, the louder the sound; a panel 8cm square is a reasonable size. The sounder must be mounted by its rim. Cut a circular card 'washer' of the same diameter as the sounder, stick this to the panel and stick the sounder to washer, as in Figure 55.

Testing: When power is switched on, the tune begins immediately and plays through once. To replay the tune, turn the power off (shut the box), then turn it on again (open the box).

Project 7 – Electronic Handkerchief Knot

In the days before paper tissues became popular, a favourite way to remember that there was *something* to be remembered (and acted upon) was to tie a knot in one's handkerchief. Sooner rather than later, the knot would be discovered and one would be reminded that there was *something* to remember. Association of ideas usually helped to remind one what that *something* was, and the knot would not be untied until what was to be done had been done. This circuit fulfils the same purpose but makes it easier to remember what the *something* is.

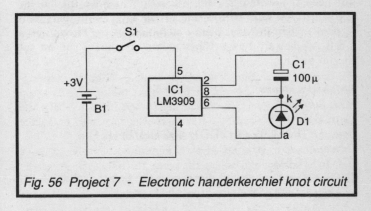

Fig. 56 Project 7 - Electronic handerkerchief knot circuit

The circuit (Fig.56) takes the form of a small box with an LED mounted on it. The LED flashes very brightly in a most

85

attention-catching way. To remind yourself, or someone else, that there is something to be done, place the flashing LED where it will remind you or them what is to be done. For example, to remind yourself to pay the electricity bill, put the unpaid bill and your cheque-book on the desk with the flashing LED on top. To remind yourself to watch a particular TV programme, stand the flashing LED on top of the TV set. If you want to leave a message in the house for somebody who is not there at the time, write the note, and put it on the table with the electronic handkerchief knot on top. When the person returns, they will soon notice that there is a message for them.

This circuit is not simply an LED flasher. The ic generates a higher voltage than that supplied by the battery and pulses this to the LED for a very short time. The result is a series of very intense flashes, about once every second.

Component notes: The circuit works with any ordinary LED, but a high-intensity LED gives a brighter flash.

Planning: The current needed is very little (less than 1mA) so the battery lasts for a long time, often for as long as 3 months of continuous running. You may decide that you do not need the switch S1, but will simply remove the battery clip when you want to turn the circuit off. A box only 8cm × 6cm × 4cm provides plenty of room, for the circuit and a 2-cell AA battery box. The standard stripboard can be cut shorter to fit.

Stripboard layout:
Size: Standard.
Cuts: G18–K18.
Pins: +V (K26), 0V (K12), D1k (G24), D1a (J24).
Capacitors: C1+ (H15), C1− (G22).
ICs: IC1 (G17).
Off-board: B1 connected directly to the board or through S1.
   Connect D1 to the pins listed above.

Panel mounting: S1, if included, D1.
   PCB assembly details are shown in Figures 57 and 58.

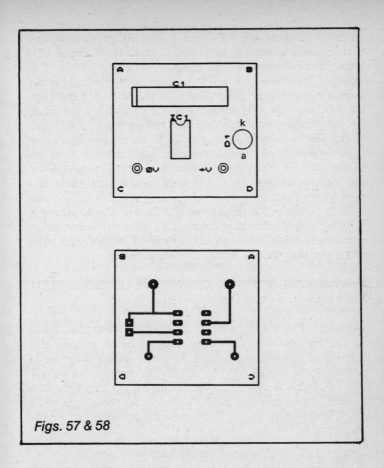

Figs. 57 & 58

Project 8 – Tooth-cleaner's Timer

It is reported that to clean your teeth really effectively you should brush them for at least 3 minutes. That is not such an easy interval to estimate, especially if you are sleepy in the mornings. This timer tells you exactly when you can stop brushing. It is geared to the bathroom environment by being just a small plastic box with no switches or other controls. Just pick it up and stand it upright: the yellow light comes on. This tells you to start brushing. Keep on brushing until the

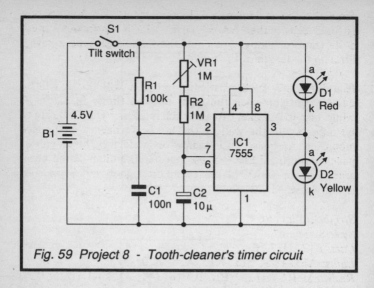

Fig. 59 Project 8 - Tooth-cleaner's timer circuit

yellow light goes out and the red light comes on. Then you can stop brushing and turn the box upside down to switch off the power.

The circuit uses the very popular timer ic, the 7555 (IC1, Fig.59). Power is controlled by a mercury tilt-switch. This is mounted inside the box so that it is on when the box is upright and off when it is upside down. Turning on the power immediately resets the timer, which then runs for 3 minutes. While it is running, the output pin 3 is high, lighting the yellow LED. At the end of the period, output goes low, causing the yellow LED to go out and the red LED to come on.

Of course, you don't *have* to use this project for tooth-timing. Use it any way that needs a single-period timer: boiling eggs, timing games moves, and many other activities.

Component notes: Tilt switches are available in a range of sizes; choose a miniature one (about 10mm long and 5mm diameter). The case is metal and there are usually two wires at one end. Some switches have only one wire and the other connection is made by wrapping bare wire around the case. Use LEDs of normal power (not high-intensity), preferably the

5mm size, one red and one yellow (or green). The battery box is for 3 cells, either AA or AAA. VR1 is a horizontal miniature trimpot, though you could use the vertical type to save a little on the length of the board.

Planning: Any small plastic project box will do; it will be quite watertight when the lid is screwed firmly in place. A white box is less likely to show the splashes. The LEDs are to be mounted in the wall of the box. We need a well-sealed mounting: use plastic 'LED clips' or, preferably, buy a pair of panel mounting LEDs. These have a chromium-plated bezel around them which makes the project look much smarter, is easily cleaned, and gives a better seal too.

Stripboard layout:
Size: Standard.
Cuts: E17–H17.
Links: A13–H13, E15–K15, A20–E20.
Resistors: R1 (A12–F12), R2 (B23–F23), VR1 (A25, B28, C25).
Pins: +V (A8), 0V (K8), D1a (A10), D1k/D2a (G10), D2k (K10).
Capacitors: C1 (F14–K14), C2+ (G23), C2– (K23).
ICs: IC1 (E16).
Blobs: F19–G19.
Off-board: From the positive of B1 to one terminal of S1. From the other terminal of S1 to pin A8. From the negative terminal of B1 to pin K8. D1 and D2 to pins listed above.

Panel mounting: See notes above on LED mounting. S1 is fixed inside the box; hold it in place with a 'Sticky Fixer'.

Testing: The only likely causes of trouble are connecting the LEDs the wrong way round and mounting the tilt switch upside down. R1 and C1 are intended to set the timer as power is switched on. Sometimes, if the switch-on is hesitant, the timer is reset and the red LED comes on. If so, switch off, wait a couple of seconds and try again. Adjust VR1 until the yellow LED comes on for 3 minutes. If you want to adapt

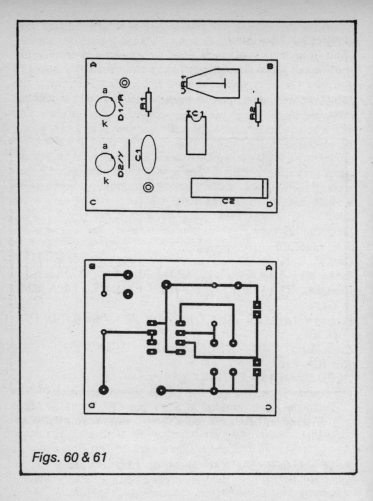

Figs. 60 & 61

the timer for shorter or longer periods, alter the value of R2. For 5 minutes it needs to be 2.2MΩ, for 10 minutes it should be about 5MΩ (4.7MΩ in series with 330kΩ, B23–D23 and D22–F22).

PCB assembly details are shown in Figures 60 and 61.

Project 9 — Door Alert

This is a loud single-tone door alert, operated by a push-button. It could also be operated by microswitch, arranged to turn on the alert when the door is opened. The project has other uses such as a room-to-room buzzer and a Morse practice set.

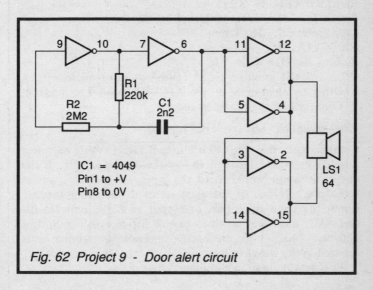

Fig. 62 Project 9 - Door alert circuit

The circuit (Fig.62) is based on a single ic which has six inverting buffers. Two are joined as an oscillator. The other four, working in two pairs, provide enough drive to make an attention-demanding sound.

Planning: This is a compact circuit and, if a miniature (38mm diameter) speaker is used, is easily housed in a small box. It operates on any voltage in the range 3V to 12V. The higher the voltage, the louder the sound. But volume is great enough with 9V, making a PP3 battery a handy power source. The volume is low with a 3V supply, though it is loud enough to be clearly heard in a quiet room with the speaker 2 or 3 metres away.

Stripboard layout:

Size: Standard.

Cuts: E19, H19. Note that most of the strips are left *uncut* beneath the ic. They join outputs and inputs of gates on opposite sides of the ic, reducing the need for wire links.

Links: C17−C22, C23−E23.

Resistors: R1 (G23−K23), R2 (H25, K25).

Pins: +V (A14), 0V (H14), LS1 (B24, E24).

Capacitors: C1 (F16−K16).

ICs: IC1 (A18).

Blobs: C18−D18, E18−F18.

Off-board: B1 positive to S1 (push-button or microswitch). Other terminal of S1 to pin A14. B1 negative to pin G14. Connect LS1 to pins listed above.

Panel mounting: LS1 (see Fig.14, p.18).

Testing: When the input to a buffer is high (+V) its output is low (0V). When the input is low the output is high. If the circuit does not work, check the input and output levels at each gate. If one of the gates seems to be acting wrongly (input the same as output, or output at a level between 0V and +V), this gives a clue. Look for fine solder bridges between adjacent copper strips. Look for components inserted in the wrong holes.

PCB details are shown in Figures 63 and 64.

Project 10 − Tantalizing Toss-up

This project is the equivalent to tossing a coin to see if it falls heads or tails, but is far more exciting. To 'toss the coin', you press and hold the push-button for a few seconds. The LED flashes very quickly: so quickly that it seems to be continuously lit. After you have released the button, the rate of flashing gradually decreases. Flashing becomes slower and slower until it eventually stops. If it stops with the LED lit, it is 'heads'. If it stops with the LED out, it is 'tails'. As far as we know, the chances of getting a head or a tail are equally likely.

IC1 (Fig.65) contains a voltage-controlled oscillator. When you press S2, the voltage at pin 9 rises to +6V and the oscillator runs fast, flashing the LED. Capacitor C2 becomes fully

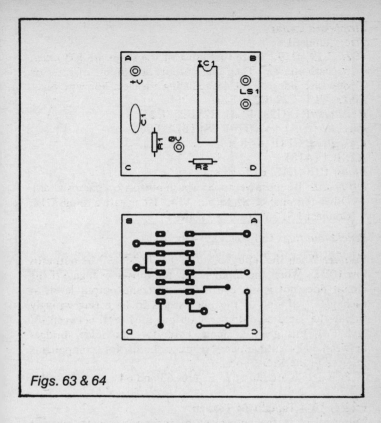

Figs. 63 & 64

charged. After you release S2, the charge on C2 leaks slowly away through R2. As the voltage on C2 falls the oscillator runs more and more slowly until it stops. This leaves the LED either on or off at the end of the run.

Component notes: Use a high-intensity LED for the best effect.

Planning: Here is a chance to design an unusual and attractive project housing. Use a tiny box or use a large one; it can be of any shape or colour that takes your fancy. Decorate it if you like — perhaps with playing cards or a cartoon of a Mississippi gambler.

93

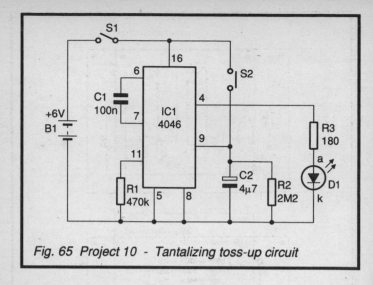

Fig. 65 Project 10 - Tantalizing toss-up circuit

Stripboard layout:
Size: Standard.
Cuts: E13, B18–J18, C21.
Links: F15–K15, C29–K29.
Resistors: R1 (C27–G27), R2 (C25–J25), R3 (E10–E15).
Pins: +V (A8), 0V/D1k (K8), D1a (E8), S2 (A27, J27).
Capacitors: C1 (G14–H11), C2+ (J23), C2– (C23).
ICs: IC1 (B17).
Blobs: A20–B20, J17–K17.
Off-board: B1 positive to S1; other terminal of S1 to pin A8.
   B1 negative to pin K8. D1 and S2 to pins listed above.

Panel mounting: S1, S2, D1.

Testing: Make sure that the strips are cut cleanly through, especially beneath the ic. Voltage at pin 9 is +6V when S2 is pressed, then takes about 1 minute to fall to 0V. LED stops flashing after about 15 seconds, when the voltage has fallen to about 1.5V. If you are using a low-impedance meter (p.62) fall in voltage is much more rapid – perhaps less than a second with very low impedance meter. The meter attachment

94

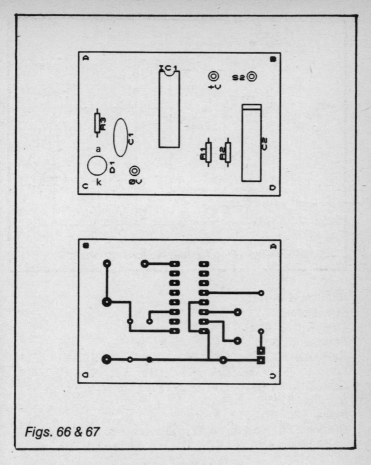

Figs. 66 & 67

of Project 19 is useful for this measurement.

PCB details are shown in Figures 66 and 67.

Chapter 7

TEN EASY PROJECTS

Here is another batch of projects for you to choose from. Most of them have more components than the projects in the previous chapter. Because of this, they are able to do some quite fascinating things. But all of them are easy to build and will normally work straight away. As in the previous chapter, we have tried to cater for a wide range of interests — take your pick!

Project 11 – Timer Bar

This is a timer with a bar-type LED display (Fig.68). The display consists of a row or bar of 8 LEDs. Pressing the RESET button extinguishes all the LEDs. Pressing the START button puts the first LED on. One minute later the next LED goes on. The LEDs light up one at a time until, 7 minutes after the start, all LEDs are illuminated. This is a process timer with many uses. It can be used for timing anything from cooking (including boiled eggs) to developing films and prints. Use it for timing phone calls. Use it for timing moves and turns in games such as chess and Scrabble.

The display is controlled by a shift register, with an LED connected to the output from each stage. Pressing S3 clears the register and all LEDs go out. Next, pressing S2 triggers the timer ic (IC1) to produce a high pulse instantly. After that it produces a short high pulse every minute. The input of the shift register (pin 1) is held high so that stage A is made high at the first clock pulse from IC1. The first LED lights. At each minute the clock pulse shifts the high level one stage along the row, lighting up the LEDs in turn.

For best results, each LED should have its own series resistor (180Ω), but this makes the wiring much more complicated. We use a single 33Ω resistor instead.

Component notes: A bargraph array of 10 LEDs is the simplest form of display, two of the LEDs being unused. Alternatively, solder individual LEDs to a piece of strip-

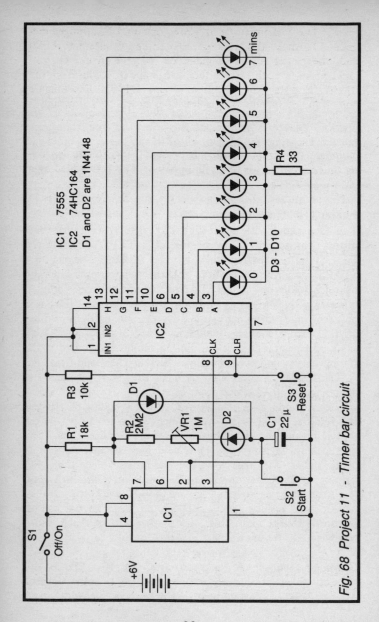

Fig. 68 Project 11 - Timer bar circuit

98

board. The LEDs may be in a row, or could be arranged in a circle. To make the minutes easier to count, alternate LEDs could be round and rectangular, or red and green. Or you could make the 5th LED different in shape or colour from the others. End-stackable arrays of 2 and 3 LEDs are available from some suppliers. A display of 3 green, 2 yellow and 3 red would give a very attractive appearance to the unit.

Planning: The circuit requires between 50 and 80mA, depending on the number of LEDs illuminated. This is provided by a battery of 4 cells; size AA alkaline cells are suitable.

If you prefer, adapt the timer to run for 3½ minutes in ½-minute intervals by substituting 10μF capacitor for C1.

Stripboard layout:

Size: Standard.

Cuts: B8—E8, D12—E12, B21—H21, C25—H25, K29, G30—J30, A31, B31, A33—K33.

Links: D3—H28, A4—E4, B5—K5, C6—J6, D11—J11, D22—K31, E22—J31, F22—H31, G22—G31, H23—K23.

Resistors: R1 (A19, C19), R2 (C20, D20), R3 (A29—G29), R4 (A37—C37), VR1 (D18, E14, F18).

Pins: +V (A3), 0V (K3), S2 (J8), S3 (G28); if LEDs mounted off-board put 8 pins at C32—K32 and 8 at C35—K35.

Capacitors: C1+ (J18), C1— (K12).

Semis: D1a (C13), D1k (J13), D2a (J20), D2k (F20), D10a—D3a (C32—K32), D10k—D3k (C35—K35).

ICs: IC1 (B7), IC2 (B24).

Blobs: A10—B10, B24—C24, A27—B27, C35—D35—E35—F35—G35—H35—J35—K35.

Off-board: Battery positive to S1; S1 to pin at A3. Battery negative to pin at K3. S2 to J8 and K3. S3 to G28 and K3. If LEDs mounted off-board connect anodes to pins at C32 —K32 and cathodes to pins at C35—K35.

Panel mounting: If the LEDs are mounted directly on the circuit board, the board is mounted in the case and an aperture cut to reveal the LEDs. If preferred, the LEDs can be mounted off-board. The end-stackable arrays are designed to

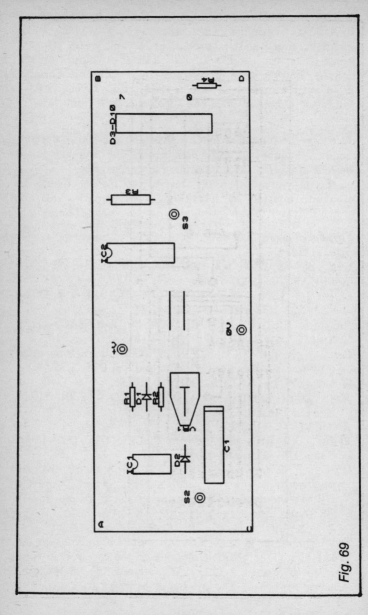

Fig. 69

100

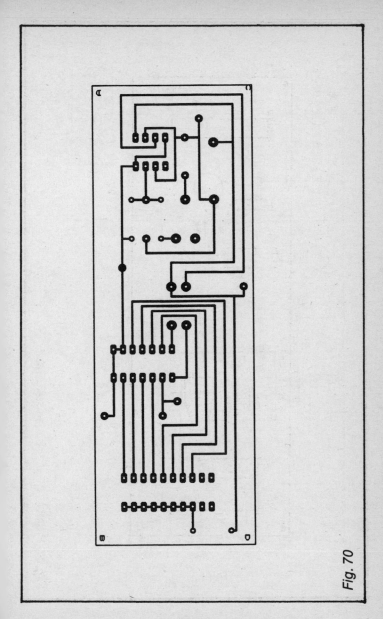

Fig. 70

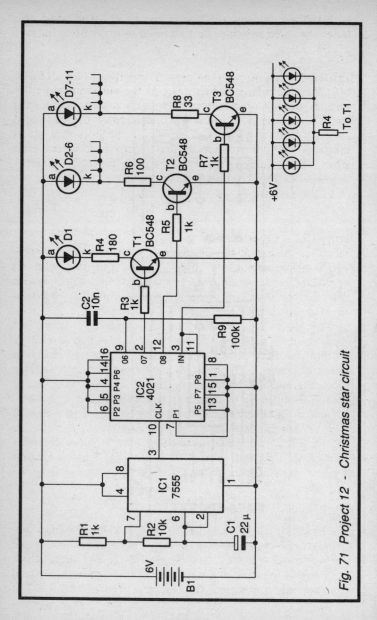

Fig. 71 Project 12 - Christmas star circuit

102

be a push-fit into an aperture in the panel. The panel also holds the three switches, best arranged in order of operation: S1, S3, S2.

Testing: Switch on S1, then press S3 briefly to turn all LEDs off. Press S2 *briefly* to light D3. At the same time, note the seconds display of a watch. D4 lights exactly 60 seconds later; if it does not, adjust VR1 and repeat the test until timing is correct. Values of tantalum capacitors vary by as much as 20%; if it happens that timing is incorrect even when VR1 is turned to one end, replace R2 with a resistor of greater (2.7MΩ) or lesser (1.8MΩ) value.

PCB details are shown in Figures 69 and 70.

Project 12 – Christmas Star

Placed at the top of the Christmas tree, or hung in a prominent position among the paper chains, this star with its exploding bands of coloured lamps contributes to the festive decorations. The same circuit can also be used to enliven a ready-made Christmas decoration.

The lamps are light-emitting diodes (p.20). These are available in a range of colours, sizes, shapes and intensities so that you have plenty of scope for designing a display to suit your tastes. The heart of the circuit is a shift register (IC2, Fig.71). When power is turned on the LOAD input (pin 9) is pulled up to logic high by C2. Registers 2, 3, 4 and 6 (inputs P2, P3, P4, P6) are connected to the 6V line so they are loaded with logic high. Registers 1, 5, 7, 8 (inputs P1, P5, P7, P8) are loaded with logic low. During the next fraction of a second, current flows from C2 through R9 and the load input becomes low. The pattern in the registers is:

L   H   H   H   L   H   L   L

The clock circuit (IC1) shifts this pattern to the right approximately twice each second. The LEDs are switched on by the outputs from registers 6 to 8 (O6, O7, O8). The output from register 8 is fed back to the serial input (pin 11) so the pattern is repeatedly circulated through the register chain. The sequence of lighting of the LEDs is:

1	*	—	—
2	—	*	—
3	*	—	*
4	*	*	—
5	*	*	*
6	—	*	*
7	—	—	*
8	—	—	—

* = LED on

The pattern spreads outward from the central LED, generating a pulsating explosion effect.

Component notes: Figure 72 shows one of many possible designs for the star. D1 is at the centre, and could be a jumbo LED. Around this a ring of 5 arrow-shaped LEDs controlled by O7. At the tips of the rays of the star are the 5

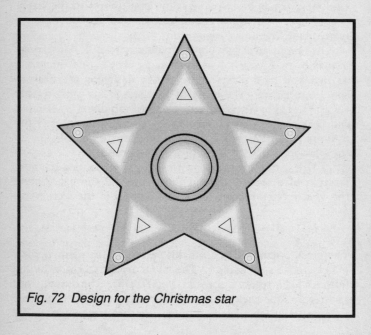

Fig. 72 Design for the Christmas star

superbright LEDs controlled by O8. You can vary the numbers of LEDs in each group and also their shape, colour and brightness. Although Figure 71 shows only one LED switched by each transistor, you will usually have 5 or some similar number connected in parallel, as shown in the inset.

Planning: The amount of current required depends on the number and power of LEDs used. A battery of 4 D-cells should be enough to run the star for several hours a day during the period from a few days before Christmas Eve to a few days after Boxing Day. The star is to be cut from hardboard, plasticard or stout card. It can be painted in bright colours, and perhaps decorated with glitter or tinsel. Design and decorate the star before you begin construction of the circuit.

Stripboard layout:

Size: Standard.

Cuts: C6—F6, C12—F12, B18—J18, C24—D24, H26—J26, B27, H31—J31, B32, H36—J36, B37.

Links: D2—E9, E2—H21, C3—K3, A4—F4, A9—C9, C13—D26, D13—C26, D14—G21, B15—H15, A16—E16, B21—D21, C22—E22, E23—K23.

Resistors: R1 (A10, D10), R2 (D11, E11), R3 (D27—J27), R4 (B30—H30), R5 (F32—J32), R6 (B35—H35), R7 (C37—J37), R8 (B39—H39), R9 (J25—K25).

Pins: +V (A1), 0V (K1), D1k (B29), D2k—D6k (B34), D7k—D11k (B38).

Capacitors: C1+ (E10), C1— (K10), C2 (A24—J24).

Semis: T1c (H29), T1b (J29), T1e (K29), T2c (H34), T2b (J34), T2e (K34), T3c (H38), T3b (J38), T3e (K38).

ICs: IC1 (C5), IC2 (B17).

Blobs: E17—F17—G17, H17—J17—K17, A20—B20.

Off-board: If the star is mounted on a Christmas tree, the battery box may be wrapped in Christmas paper to look like a present and fixed in the fork of one of the stouter branches. No switch is provided; either remove the cells from the battery holder, or solder a crocodile clip to the positive supply wire and clip this to the positive tag of the battery holder when power is required. Bore two small

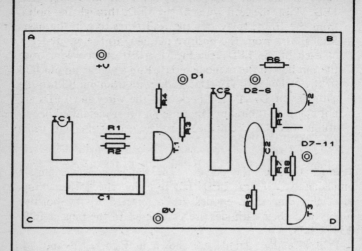

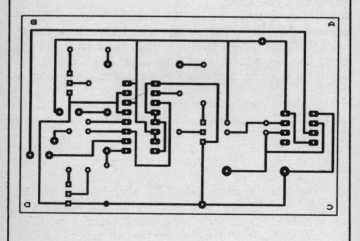

Figs. 73 & 74

106

holes in the star base 2.5mm apart for mounting each LED. Push the lead wires of the LEDs through the holes, from the front; splay out the lead wires to grip the base. Run a wire from the positive pin (A1) to the anode leads of each of the LEDs (see Fig.51, p.79). Run a wire from the pin B29 to the cathode of D1. Run a wire from pin B34 to the cathodes of D2–D6. Run a wire from pin B38 to the cathodes of D7–D11. Check that the wires and LEDs are not being short-circuited by tinsel or other metallised decorations. Fix the circuit board to the rear of the star, using Blutack.

Testing: Connect the power. The sequence begins almost immediately. If any LEDs fail to light, check the wiring, especially that their anodes are connected to the positive supply and their cathodes are connected to the pins at B29, B34 or B38.

PCB assembly details are shown in Figures 73 and 74.

Project 13 – Fire Alarm

This circuit switches on an audible alarm when it detects excessive heat. It is designed to respond when the temperature of its surroundings are greater than about 60°C. This is hotter than the normal room temperature and indicates that something is wrong, probably that something in the room is ablaze.

The circuit uses a *thermistor* (p.13), shown as TH1 in Figure 75. The resistance of the thermistor used in this project is about 47kΩ at normal room temperature (25°C) but decreases to about 11kΩ at 60°C. As its resistance goes down, the voltage at point A in the circuit rises. The change in voltage is detected by T1, and this controls the thyristor T2. The circuit is set to detect fire when both S1 and S2 are closed. If the thermistor becomes hot, the voltage at A rises and the AWD and lamp are suddenly switched on. Once they have switched on, they are switched off only by opening S2, or by opening S1 to turn off the power. So the alarm sounds until someone hears it and comes to take action.

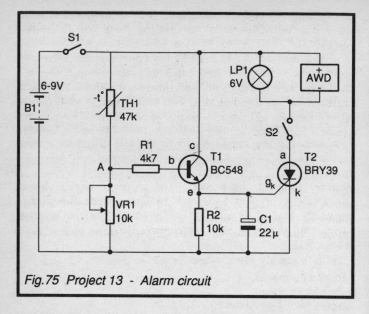

Fig.75 Project 13 - Alarm circuit

Component notes: TH1 is a bead thermistor with a resistance of 47kΩ at 25°C. T2 is a BRY39, a versatile semiconductor device which we are using here as a silicon-controlled switch. It has four terminal wires (see Fig.15, p.19) of which one (the anode gate, g_a) is not used in this project. Either cut the wire short or solder it to the board where indicated.

Planning: The circuit works on 6V or 9V and takes less than 1mA when it is set to detect fire. It takes rather more when the thermistor becomes really hot and the AWD and lamp are turned on. Most of the time it will be taking less than 1mA and a battery of AA alkaline cells will last nearly 3 months.

Decide where to locate the thermistor, the main circuit with lamp, and the AWD. The thermistor can be mounted on the circuit board, but make sure that there are plenty of holes in the box to allow hot air or smoke to enter and warm the thermistor. Or you can put the thermistor in any convenient spot — even in another room — with a pair of wires to connect it to the circuit board. Locate it where you think a fire is most likely to begin. It is usually best to mount the thermistor high up in the room so that the rising hot air heats it quickly.

Similarly, the AWD may be mounted on the board for convenience, or it may be located in a central place, such as a hall-way, where it is most easily heard throughout the house. Perhaps, before deciding this, you should decide what type of AWD to use. There are small (about 25mm diameter and 15mm deep) and inexpensive (less than £1) piezo sounders which produce a penetrating high-pitched screech. A little more expensive are mini-sirens which give two-tone or pulsed-tone sounds, which are more attention-catching. There are larger (10cm diameter) sirens costing up to £10, which produce very loud wailing sounds and will readily wake a whole houseful of people. Any of these types can be used with this project; but make sure that the AWD is intended to run on 6V DC.

Stripboard layout:

Size: Standard.

Cuts: C14.

Links: G19–K19.

Resistors: R1 (C8, D8), R2 (E9, K9), TH1 (A5, D5).

Pins: +V (A3), 0V (K3), VR1wa (D3), VR1b (K5), AWD+/LP1 (A21), S2 (C23).

Capacitors: C1+ (E13), C1− (K13).

Semis: T1c (A11), T1b (C11), T1e (E11), T2a (C17), T2k (G17), T2g$_k$ (E19), T2g$_a$ (B19).

Off-board: B1 with negative terminal wired to 0V pin and positive terminal to S1. Other terminal of S1 goes to +V pin. VR1, connected where listed. AWD and LP1, wired in parallel between A21 and one terminal of S2, but note that it is better not to connect the AWD until the circuit has been tested. S2, other terminal wired to pin at C23.

Panel-mounting: S1, S2, VR1, socket for LP1, possibly AWD.

Notes: There is space on the right end of the board for mounting a small AWD; if you are mounting the AWD on the board, solder its terminals to suitable copper strips and run a wire link from A21 to its positive terminal, and from S2 to its negative terminal. Cut strips if necessary, so that the AWD is not connected to other parts of the circuit. The thermistor TH1 is included in the resistor list; if this is to be mounted off-board, insert pins at A5 and D5 and wire the thermistor to these.

Testing: Do not wire in the AWD yet, as the noise made during testing can be very distracting to everyone in the house. Connect a voltmeter to point A (pin D3 on stripboard) and to 0V. Turn VR1 fully to the left. Close S1 and S2. The voltage at A is 0V. Turn VR1 slowly right; when the voltage at A reaches about 1V, the lamp comes on. Note this triggering voltage. Open S2, the lamp goes off. Turn VR1 fully left, close S2; the lamp remains off. To set the alarm for fire detection, open S2. Put the thermistor against something hot, such as an electric lamp, or in a cup of water at 60°C (beware scalding water!) and leave it for a few seconds to warm up. Then adjust VR1 until the voltage is just at the triggering voltage. Remove the thermistor from the hot place and close S2. Now replace the thermistor in the hot place; the voltage rises to 1V and the lamp comes on. Finally, wire in the AWD and repeat the checks made above.

PCB assembly details are shown in Figures 76 and 77.

Project 14 – Night Light
Young children may fall asleep more happily if there is a low-level light burning in the room. When this circuit is set, the main lamp provides a reasonable amount of light for a period of about 20 minutes. By the end of this time, it is likely that the child will be asleep. The main lamp switches off silently, but a very low-level lamp continues to burn, in case the child should wake. The circuit is connected to a large touch-plate mounted beside the bed or cot. The touch-plate is large enough to be easily located in dim light. The slightest contact with this plate turns on the main lamp for a further period of 20 minutes.

The touch switch consists of T1 and R3 (Fig.78). When the plate is touched with a finger, the voltage at the drain (d)

110

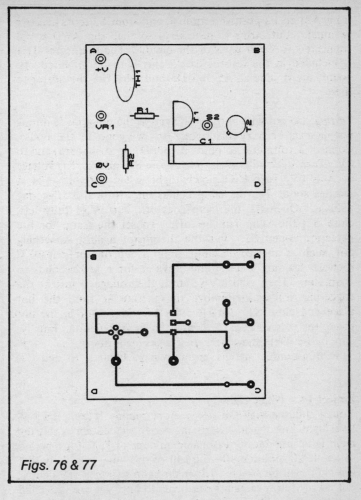

Figs. 76 & 77

of T1 falls briefly, triggering the timer IC1. This ic is specially intended for long-period timing. When triggered, its output at pin 3 goes high. This turns on T2, causing current to flow through the main lamp LP1. The output stays high for a period depending on the values of R4 and C2. In this circuit this period is fixed at approximately 22 minutes. To obtain

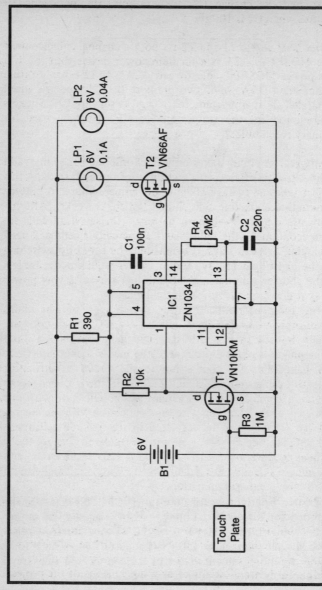

Fig. 78 Project 14 - Night-light circuit

other periods, change C2; for example, the period is 10 minutes when C2 is 100nF.

Component notes: T1 and T2 are both n-channel enhancement type MOSFETs. T1 is a medium-power device, but T2 is a high-power MOSFET able to carry 2A. If LP1 has a rating greater than 0.1A, or if two or more 0.1A lamps are wired in parallel, it is important to fit a heat sink to T2. Sockets are required for the lamps, usually MES (such as used for ordinary torch bulbs).

Planning: The circuit takes only 6mA but the lamps may add 140mA to this. Based on a nightly run from 6pm to 8am, this project takes an average of about 0.7 ampere-hours. A battery of four D-size alkaline cells should last for 3 weeks. Alternatively use a 991, 6V lantern battery. D-size Nicad cells are more economical; the industrial 4 ampere-hour cells will need recharging every 5 days. Current may be saved by switching off the night light at, say, 10pm. Power requirements are less in the shorter summer nights. Another way of saving power is to cut down on the power of the lamps.

The most economical power source is a plug-in mains power-supply unit (PSU), producing 6V DC. Such units are usually housed in a plastic case which incorporates a 3-pin mains plug. It plugs directly into the mains socket and there is a light cable for connection to the circuit. With most units the cable ends in a multiple connector. You need to provide a connector for the circuit which will mate with one of these. Check that you wire the connection with the correct polarity. PSUs may be regulated or unregulated (cheaper). The PSU for this project need not be regulated because the ic includes its own regulator. A 300mA PSU is adequate, and this allows a second 0.1A lamp to be wired in parallel with LP1 to give greater illumination.

Before beginning construction, consider what form the project will take. This will partly depend on whether power is to come from a battery or from a PSU. In its simplest form, the circuit is enclosed in a box, with the two lamps in sockets mounted on top of the box. For a young child, it is possible to devise all kinds of exciting versions of the project.

113

Perhaps the lamps could be enclosed in a 'mushroom' made from creamy-coloured translucent plastic or papier maché, so as to cast a more even glow on the surroundings. The area below the mushroom could be populated by model dwarfs or fairies. Another idea is to house an imaginative model scene in an open-sided box, using the lamps to illuminate this. Or a ready-made model or toy could be used as a mount for the lamps — perhaps a small teddy-bear holding a lamp in each of its paws.

Stripboard layout:
Size: Standard.
Cuts: H18–J18, C21–J21, H27–J27.
Links: C12–H12, B15–F15, E18–J29.
Resistors: R1 (A12–B12), R2 (B13–C13), R3 (J16–K16), R4 (C25–D25).
Pins: +V (A10), 0V (K10), LP1 (H34).
Capacitors: C1 (F19–J19), C2 (D26–K26).
Semis: T1d (H14), T1g (J14), T1s (K14), T2d (H31), T2g (J31), T2s (K31).
ICs: IC1 (C20).
Blobs: F20–G20, J20–K20, E23–F23.
Off-board: Positive line from battery or PSU to A10; negative line to K10. LP1 between A10 and H34. LP2 between A10 and K10. Touch-plate is square or rectangle of sheet aluminium or other metal, approx. 6cm^2. Or use any other metal object such as large nut or washer, bracket, or rod; connect to J12 with insulated wire up to 30cm long. Touch-plate must be insulated from ground; mount on plastic or wood.

Testing: Use 4.7nF capacitor to replace C2 while testing. LP1 is off when power switched on. Touching the plate turns it on and it stays on for 30 seconds. Check that T2 does not overheat; if it does, fit a (larger) heat sink. LP2 is on continuously. When all is working correctly, replace C2 with capacitor of suitable value, depending on the period required.

PCB assembly details are shown in Figures 79 and 80.

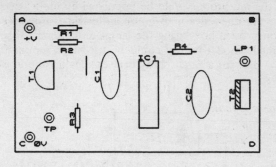

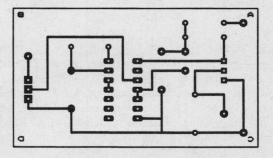

Figs. 79 & 80

Project 15 – Space Gun

This is a project to build for a younger member of the family.
Its success depends partly on your inventiveness at making
the gun-shaped housing. A visit to a DIY store to inspect the
shelves of plumbers' fittings will yield some useful basic parts.

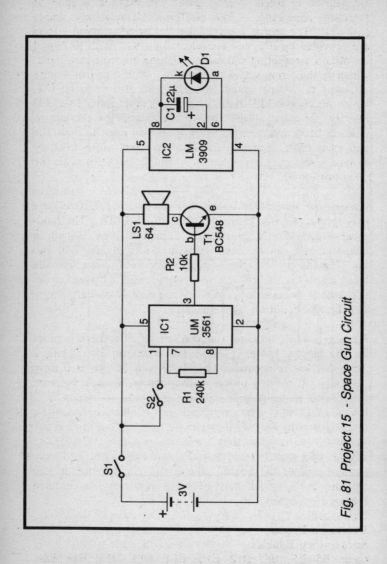

Fig. 81 Project 15 - Space Gun Circuit

These plus other oddments and pieces cut from plastic boxes, all painted in bright enamel paint will make a weapon of fearsome appearance. The electronics is relatively simple (Fig.81). The gun is triggered by closing S1. Sound effects are provided by IC1, and are selected by S2. With S2 closed we obtain a repeating and rather whining machine-gun sound, which is the firing sound of the gun. With S2 open a quite different siren-type sound is heard. S1 also turns on IC2, which makes the LED flash brightly at a rapid rate. This LED may be mounted at the end of the muzzle of the gun to indicate 'stun rays' coming from it. If you want to make the gun even more impressive, add up to eight more LEDs of various sizes, shapes and colours, and drive them with the circuit of Project 12.

Component notes: D1 could be a jumbo-sized LED or you may prefer to use a smaller ultra-bright LED. The loud-speaker has a 64Ω coil; use a miniature type, 38mm in diameter. It can be fixed with three sets of nut, bolt and tag (Fig.14, p.18). S1 is a lever-action microswitch, the lever acting as the trigger; use epoxy resin adhesive to fix the switch in position. S2 can be a slide switch, toggle switch or push-button, as preferred.

Planning: When building the gun, make sure there is room for the battery holder. The circuit works on 3V, so only a 2-cell battery is needed. The circuit can be powered from AA cells. If the toy proves really popular, it might be more suitable to make it large enough to contain a battery of 2 type C or D cells. The stripboard and pcb have been kept as small as possible so that they can be fitted into a small space. The pcb is designed so that it can be cut across along the line XX. If you want to build only the sound generator, etch only the left half of the board. The circuit can be built in two separate parts, which may fit more easily into a confined space.

Stripboard layout:
Size: 6 rows, 22 holes.
Cuts: B5–E5, B8, D10–E10, E14, C15–D15, B18–E18.

117

Links: D8–F8, B21–F21.

Resistors: R1 (D3–E3), R2 (C11–E11).

Pins: +V (A1), 0V (F1), S2 (E9).

Capacitors: C1+ (D22), C1– (E16).

Semis: T1c (D12), T1b (E12), T1e (F12), D1a (C16), D1k (E15).

ICs: IC1 (B4), IC2 (B17). These are the positions of pin 5 of each ic, the ics being mounted the other way round to the usual, with pin 1 on row E.

Blobs: A4–B4, A17–B17.

Off-board: Battery positive to S1; S1 to A1. S2 to E9 and A1. LS1 to D14 and A1. D1 as above.

Panel mounting: This depends on the parts used for the enclosure. Mount D1 on the end of the barrel. Mount the speaker at the rear or on one side; firm mounting is essential for maximum volume. The speaker can be hidden inside the gun, with holes drilled to allow the sound to escape.

PCB assembly details are shown in Figures 82 and 83.

Project 16 – Are you alert?

This project measures your reaction time to the nearest tenth of a second. It can be adapted to measure with even greater precision. The LED seven-segment display shows numbers between 0 and 9 (Fig.84). Your friend resets the device to zero by holding down a push-button (S2). You concentrate on watching the display, with your finger on button S3, but not pressing it down. When the friend releases S2, the display begins to count up in tenths of a second. As soon as you see the display begin to count, you press button S3, which stops it. You can then read your response time in tenths of a second.

Component notes: IC2 is a counter which converts the count into the signals required to drive the segments of the display. The display may be of any size; the designs given here are suited to a popular 0.3-inch *low-current* display. Note that this *must* be of the *common cathode* type, not common anode. Figure 85 shows the pin connections as seen from the front. In Figure 85, the display is in a 14-pin dil socket,

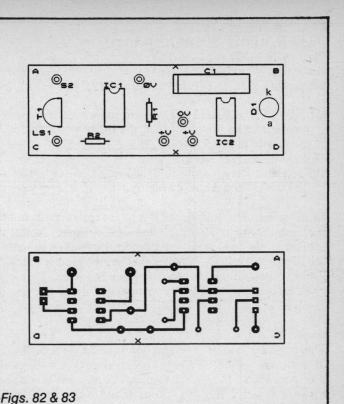

Figs. 82 & 83

but the top and bottom pair of sockets are not used. It is mounted on a small rectangle of stripboard, with terminal pins for connections to the main circuit.

Planning: The circuit is powered by a battery of four type AA, C or D cells, and housed in a plastic box.

Stripboard layout:
Size: Standard.
Cuts: B12–E12, C18–F18, C20, G20, B27–J27, H31.
Links: D7–J31, B8–K8, C9–D15, A10–E10, G24–K24.

119

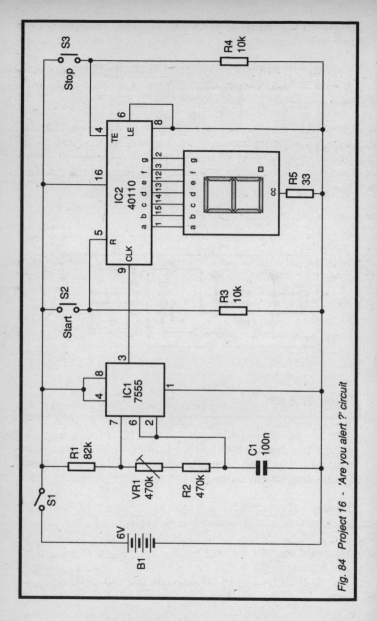

Fig. 84 Project 16 - 'Are you alert?' circuit

120

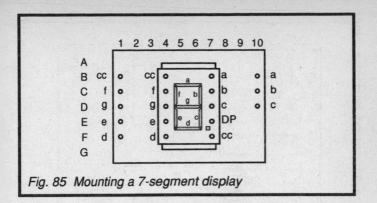

Fig. 85 Mounting a 7-segment display

Resistors: R1 (A16–C16), R2 (D16–G16), R3 (F23–K23), R4 (E21–K21), R5 (H32–K32), VR1 (C17, C19, G18).

Pins: +V (A3), 0V (K3), S2 (F22), S3 (E20). Display segments: a (B20), b (C31), c (D34), d (E31), e (F34), f (D24), g (C22), common cathode (H34).

Capacitors: C1 (C5–K5).

ICs: IC1 (B11), IC2 (B26).

Blobs: A14–B14, J26–K26, A29–B29.

Off-board: Battery positive to S1; S1 to A3. Battery negative to K3. S2 to F22 and A3. S3 to E20 and A3. Display connections as listed above.

Panel mounting: In the stripboard version the display is mounted on a separate board, as in Figure 85; cut the strips at B5 to F5. This board is mounted behind an aperture on the panel. Glue it in place, or use small bolts.

The pcb version provides for mounting the display directly on the board. But note that, to simplify the track layout, the socket is soldered to the rear (copper side) of the board. It is better not to drill holes for the pins of the socket but to stand the socket on its pins on the rear of the board, and solder each pin to its pad. If you prefer to mount the display on a separate board (Fig.85), drill holes in the pcb where the socket is supposed to be and solder terminal pins into these holes. Then join each pin to the corresponding pin on the display board.

121

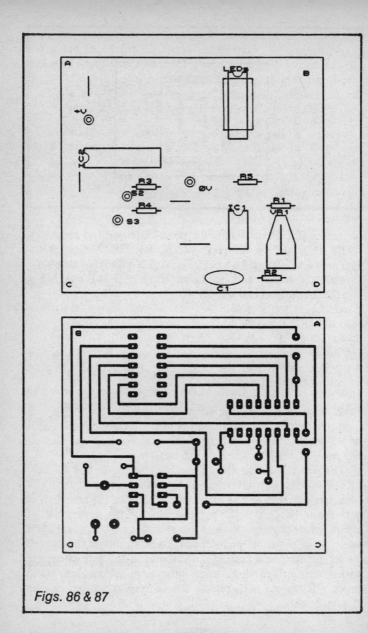

Figs. 86 & 87

122

Mount S1 and S3 on the panel, S3 preferably just below the display. S2 may be mounted on the panel but is best joined to the circuit by a long lead, so that it may be hidden from the subject being tested. With a long lead, S2 could be in a separate room, making it impossible for the subject to anticipate exactly when the display will start changing.

Testing: If the display shows strange symbols instead of numbers, check the connections between the pins on the main board and those on the display board. To adjust the timing, switch on the power and let the display cycle through its normal sequence. Watch segment c, which is on for all numbers except 2. By measuring how long it takes for c to blink off, say, 100 times, you can measure the length of 100 cycles. This should take 10 seconds; if it does not, adjust VR1. If you have fast reactions and find that you rarely take longer than 3s to respond, try making the clock run faster. Substitute a 47nF capacitor for C1 and adjust VR1 to produce 200 cycles in 10s.

PCB assembly details are shown in Figures 86 and 87.

Project 17 – Blinkers
This attention-catching circuit was designed for use in a model railway system, to flash the red lights at a level crossing. It can be used in many other situations where the purpose is to warn or remind. Use it to draw attention to a notice or to a low head-splitting beam or doorway. Use it as a door alert for a deaf person.

The circuit requires only one ic consisting of four NAND gates (Fig.88). Two are wired as an astable. The outputs of these gates are connected to two more gates. These provide the current for driving the LEDs without drawing excessive current from the astable and preventing it from operating correctly.

Component notes: The capacitor is a polyester type. The LEDs can be any type, including ultra-bright, but not flashing LEDs. Miniature LEDs 3mm in diameter are suitable for use in models, but sub-miniature LEDs, 2.2mm in diameter, are obtainable from a few suppliers.

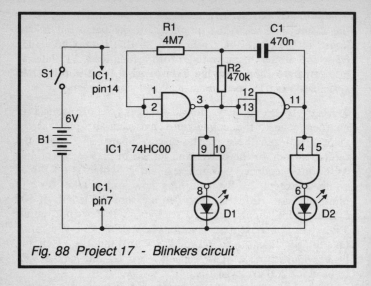

Fig. 88 Project 17 - Blinkers circuit

Planning: The circuit requires 10mA, so it can operate on a battery. It can be powered from any *direct current* (DC) supply used in connection with a model railway, but not from an alternating (AC) supply. It can be powered from a supply of higher voltage (9V or 12V) but then you should wire resistors in series with the LEDs. Use 330Ω resistors with a 9V supply and 1kΩ resistors with a 12V supply.

If the circuit is to be run for extended periods as a warning display, it is more economical to power it from a 6V unregulated DC mains unit (p.113).

When used with a railway or other model, the circuit board can usually be concealed in the scenery or beneath the base board. Wires run from the circuit board to the lamps.

Stripboard layout:
Size: Standard or (for concealing in a small space) 10 rows by 13 holes.
Cuts: C8–D8, G8–J8.
Links: A11–C11, E11–G11.
Resistors: R1 (B5–C5), R2 (B3–E3).
Pins: +V (A1), 0V (K1), D1a (J13), D2a (H3).

Capacitors: C1 (B13–F13).
ICs: IC1 (C7).
Blobs: C7–D7, F7–G7, J7–K7, D10–E10, G10–H10.
Off-board: Battery positive to S1 (optional); S1 to A1. Battery
negative to K1. D1a and D2a to pins listed above; D1k
and D2k to K1.

Testing: If LEDs fail to light, check that they are mounted the
right way round. Note: strips E and F are *not* cut under the
ic. For a slower flashing rate, use a capacitor of larger
capacity.

PCB assembly details are shown in Figure 89 and 90.

Project 18 – Frost Detector
This not only sounds an alarm when the temperature falls
below freezing point, but can be set to come on at any temperature which is lower than normal. Use this project in the
garden or greenhouse to warn you when frost is imminent, in
plenty of time to cover up delicate plants. Or use it to warn
you when you have forgotten to close the greenhouse venti-
lators at the end of a hot sunny day. If your central heating
system is heated by solid fuel, this circuit will warn you when
the fire needs stoking.

The circuit (Fig.91) is the same as that for the Fire Alarm
(Project 13) except that VR1 and TH1 change places and
that we now use a 1MΩ pot as VR1, instead of 10kΩ.

Planning: Except when the alarm is sounding, the circuit
requires only 150μA. A battery of four AA size alkaline cells
lasts for a year or more. Read the *Component notes* and
Planning section of Project 13 before building this project.
For maximum exposure to cold, the thermistor should be
mounted close to ground level and should be shaded from
direct sunlight.

Stripboard layout:
Size: Standard.
Cuts: C14.
Links: G19–K19.

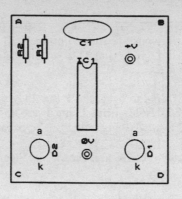

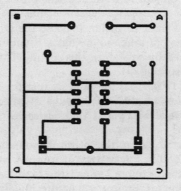

Figs. 89 & 90

126

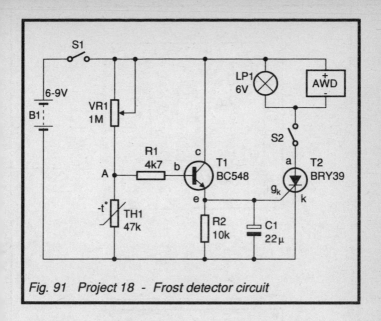

Fig. 91   Project 18 - Frost detector circuit

Resistors: R1 (C8–D8), R2 (E9–K9), TH1 (D3–K5).

Pins: +V (A3), 0V (K3), VR1a (D5), VR1bw (A5), AWD+/
LP1 (A21), S2 (C23).

Capacitors: C1+ (E13), C1– (K13).

Semis: T1c (A11), T1b (C11), T1e (E11), T2a (C17), T2k
(G17), T2g$_k$ (E19), T2g$_a$ (B19).

Off-board: B1 with negative terminal wired to 0V pin and
positive terminal to S1. Other terminal of S1 goes to +V
pin. VR1, connected where listed. AWD and LP1, wired
in parallel between A21 and one terminal of S2, but note
that it is better not to connect the AWD until the circuit
has been tested. S2, other terminal wired to pin at C23.

Panel-mounting: S1, S2, VR1, socket for LP1, possibly AWD.

Notes: There is space on the right end of the board for mounting a small AWD; if you are mounting the AWD on the board,
solder its terminals to suitable copper strips and run wire
links from A21 to its positive terminal, and from S2 to its

127

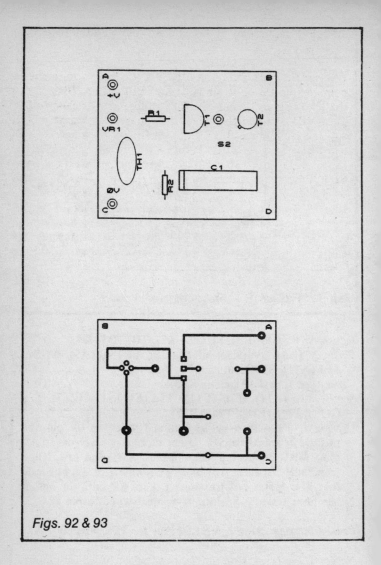

Figs. 92 & 93

negative terminal. Cut strips if necessary, so that the AWD is not connected to other parts of the circuit. The thermistor TH1 is included in the resistor list; if this is to be mounted off-board, insert pins at D3 and K5 and wire the thermistor to these.

Testing: Do not wire in the AWD yet. Connect a voltmeter to point A (pin D3 on stripboard) and to 0V. Turn VR1 fully to the left. Close S1 and S2. The voltage at A is close to 0V. Turn VR1 slowly right; when the voltage at A reaches about 1V, the lamp comes on. Note this triggering voltage. Open S2, the lamp goes off. Turn VR1 fully left, close S2; the lamp remains off. To set the alarm for frost detection, open S2. Immerse the thermistor in a glass of water, in which several ice cubes are floating and leave it for a few minutes to cool. Then adjust VR1 until the voltage is just at the triggering voltage. Remove the thermistor from the iced water and close S2. Now replace the thermistor in the iced water; the voltage rises to 1V and the lamp comes on. Now wire in the AWD and repeat the checks made above.

PCB assembly details are shown in Figures 92 and 93.

Project 19 – Voltmeter Probe
Consider the circuit shown in Figure 94. The formula on p.29 tells us that the voltage at point A is 2V. If you connect a digital voltmeter or multimeter between point A and the 0V line, you obtain a reading of almost exactly 2V. This is

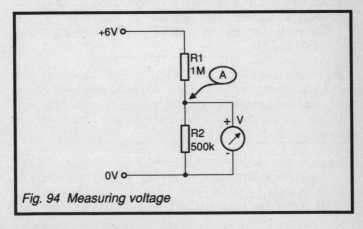

Fig. 94 Measuring voltage

129

because such a meter has high *input impedance*. It draws almost no current from the circuit while the measurement is being taken. But many of the cheaper voltmeters are moving-coil meters. When connected to a circuit, current flows through the coil of the meter. In the cheapest such meters, the resistance of the coil may be only 20kΩ when the meter is switched to its 10V range. The coil acts like a 20kΩ resistor connected in parallel with R2. The effect is to give the lower part of the circuit a resistance of only 19.2kΩ instead of 500kΩ. The result is that the voltage at A drops from 2V to 0.11V. Clearly, the measurement is absolutely useless. This difficulty always arises when we use a low-impedance voltmeter on a circuit in which resistances are relatively high.

If your voltmeter has low input impedance (quoted on the dial or in the handbook as 2000Ω/V) or even medium impedance (10 000Ω/V), this circuit will improve the accuracy of its measurements considerably. The circuit has an input impedance of $10^{12}\,\Omega$ (ten million million ohms), putting it in the same class at the more expensive digital meters.

The input voltage is fed to an operational amplifier (IC1, Fig.95). This amplifier is connected so that its output voltage is exactly the same as its input voltage. It is a *voltage follower* (p.33). The point about using the amplifier is that it takes virtually no current into its input, but is able to deliver enough current from its output to drive the meter. The other ic is a voltage inverter. It is fed with +9V and converts this to −9V to provide a negative supply required by the op amp.

This probe unit can be used to measure any DC voltage from 0V up to 9V.

Component notes: C1 and C2 are electrolytic capacitors with radial leads (both wires at the same end) in the stripboard version and axial leads in the pcb version, see Fig.13, p.15. Take great care to connect the capacitors the right way round. D1 is a *germanium* diode.

Planning: The circuit requires less than 1mA making a 9V PP3 battery a satisfactory power source that will last for hours. This means that the circuit can be housed in a small case, and the circuit board has been designed small enough to allow this.

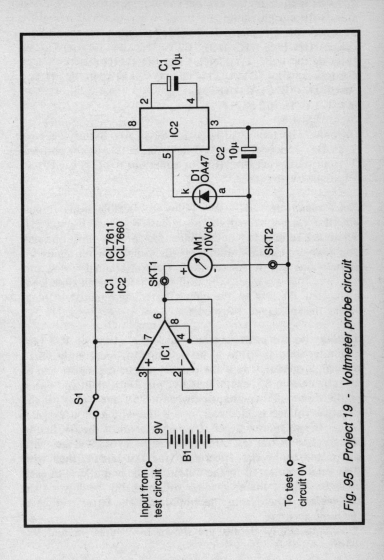

Fig. 95 Project 19 - Voltmeter probe circuit

131

Stripboard layout:

Size: 8 strips × 26 holes.

Cuts: C6–F6, E11, C15–D15, F15, C22–F22.

Links: D3–E9, A10–D10, E20–H20, B4–F4, A25–C25.

Pins: +V (A1), 0V (H1), INPUT (E1), OUTPUT (E10).

Capacitors: C1+ (D17), C1– (F17), C2+ (E12), C2– (C12).

Semis: D1a (B26), D1k (F26).

ICs: IC1 (C5), IC2 (C21).

Blobs: B8–C8.

Off-board: Battery positive to S1; S1 to A1. Battery negative to H1. Input lead to E1. Lead from E10 to meter positive; from meter negative (0V, or common) to H1. Lead from circuit 0V to H1.

Panel mounting: S1. Two holes for flexible leads (input, circuit 0V), connected to the circuit board at E1 and H1. These are terminated in crocodile clips or test clips, one red, one blue or black. Mount on the panel two terminals for connections to the meter leads (screw terminal posts, one red, one blue or black), or drill two holes for flexible leads connected directly to the circuit board, terminated in plugs fitting the sockets on the meter.

Testing: Before switching on, check the wiring of IC2 very carefully, as it is liable to be destroyed if incorrectly wired up. In particular, check the polarity of the capacitors and of D1. Switch on S1; check that IC1 pin 7 is at +9V, and pins 4 and 8 are at –9V (perhaps between –8.5V and –9V). If the negative voltage is incorrect, check the wiring of IC2 again.

Set the voltmeter to its 10V range; connect the 0V line to the 0V line of the test circuit. Measure several voltages with the meter connected directly to the test circuit, then with the meter connected to the output of the amplifier. In each case, the direct meter reading will probably be lower than the reading taken from the amplifier. The latter reading is the more accurate.

PCB assembly details are shown in Figures 96 and 97.

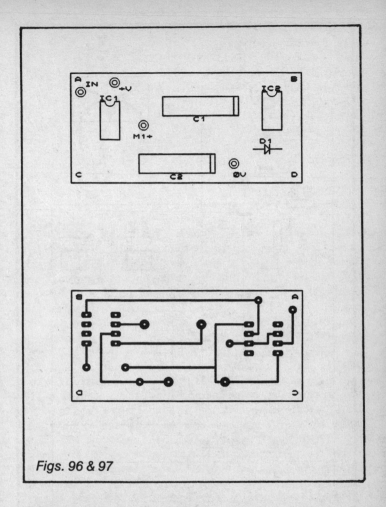

Figs. 96 & 97

Project 20 — Master–slave Intercom

A master–slave intercom has two stations; the controlling station is the master and, when the switch is set to SEND, the person at the master station talks to the person at the slave station. Having spoken the message, the person at the master station switches to RECEIVE to listen to the reply from the slave. This system is not quite as convenient as a

133

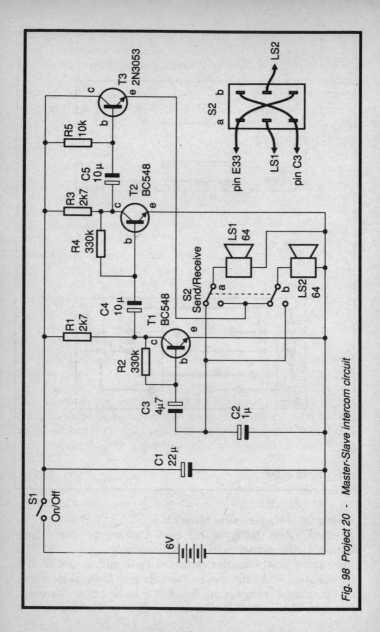

Fig. 98 Project 20 - Master-Slave intercom circuit

full two-way system but it is much simpler to build and requires only a pair of wires between the two stations.

The intercom uses two loudspeakers, which double as microphones (Fig.98). All of the circuitry except LS2 (the slave speaker) are housed in the enclosure of the master. With S2 switched to SEND, sound picked up by LS1 produces a signal which is amplified by T1 and by T2. T3 provides the power (larger current) to drive LS2, which is in the enclosure of the slave. When S2 is switched to RECEIVE, signals from LS2 in the slave are fed to the amplifiers and the output from T3 goes to LS1. We have simply interchanged the connections to the two speakers.

Component notes: LS1 and LS2 are so-called 'high-impedance' speakers, with a coil resistance of 64Ω. The circuit does not work with low-impedance (8Ω, 15Ω) speakers. Miniature speakers (38mm diameter) work well, and allow a small enclosure to be used. S2 is a double-pole double-throw (DPDT) switch; it may be a toggle switch or slide switch, whichever you prefer. Note that T3 is a medium-power npn transistor.

Planning: The circuit takes about 20mA. Unless you (at the master station) are expecting a message from the slave and so are waiting with S2 switched to RECEIVE, there is no need to turn on the power supply except when you are ready to send a message. A battery holder with four AA cells lasts for about 100 hours of continuous operation. This can easily be fitted into a small enclosure, making a very compact unit.

Stripboard layout:
Size: Standard.
Cuts: C20, F20, H20.
Resistors: R1 (A14–F14), R2 (F15–H15), R3 (A26–F26), R4 (F27–H27), R5 (A33–C33).
Pins: +V (A3), 0V (K3), S2 (C3 and E33).
Capacitors: C1+ (A6), C1– (K6), C2+ (C8), C2– (K8), C3+ (H10), C3– (C10), C4+ (F17), C4– (H22), C5+ (F29), C5– (C32).
Semis: T1c (F12), T1b (H12), T1e (K12), T2c (F24), T2b

(H24), T2e (K24), T3c (A35), T3b (C35), T3e (E35).
Off-board: Battery positive to S1; S1 to pin A3. Battery negative to K3. S2 to pins C3 and E33 (see inset to Fig. 98), LS1 between S2 and pin K3. LS2 between S2 and pin K3, using a pair of flexible wires running from the master to the slave.

Panel mounting: The master panel has S1, S2 and LS1 mounted on it. The slave panel has only LS2. Mount the speakers firmly to obtain maximum volume (see Fig.14).

Testing: The voltage at the collectors of T1 and T2 is 3V, when there is no signal. Owing to component tolerances, it may possibly be between 2V and 4V, which is acceptable. If it is outside this range on either of these transistors, it may give rise to distortion. The voltage can be increased by increasing the value of the resistor between collector and base (R2 or R4). The voltage is decreased by decreasing R2 or R4. The voltage at the *emitter* of T3 should ideally be 3V in the absence of a signal, but may lie between 2V and 4V. The voltage is increased by decreasing the value of R5, or decreased by increasing its value. Should the loudspeakers emit a buzzing or whistling sound, or perhaps a slow 'put-put-put' sound ('motor-boating'), this is because part of the circuit is in continuous oscillation. Electrolytic capacitors vary widely in value and it may happen that one of those you are using has a value that makes the circuit oscillate. The cure is to substitute a capacitor of higher or lower value. Try increasing C1 to 47μF, or C2 to 2.2μF. Another suggestion is to connect a 10nF capacitor between the collector of T1 and the ground rail (F16 to K16 on the stripboard layout).

PCB assembly details are shown in Figures 99 and 100.

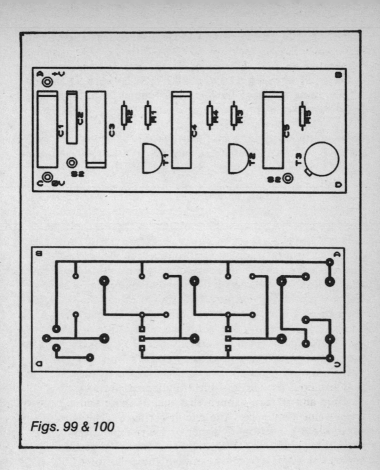

Figs. 99 & 100

137

Chapter 8

TEN CHALLENGING PROJECTS

The projects in this third batch are either more complicated to build or need more careful alignment than those in earlier chapters. But, after you have had experience in building a few of the projects from earlier chapters, you should have no difficulty with these. As before, there are some ingenious circuits, doing fascinating things. Choose the ones which interest you most.

Project 21 — Lie Detector

The human skin is slightly moist at most times and is able to conduct an electric current. If we are nervous, embarrassed, or excited, there is a slight increase in the activity of the sweat glands, making the skin moister than usual. This makes it conduct electricity more easily. We use this effect to detect if a person is telling lies, or reacting to some other situation which slightly increases the rate of sweating. The subject of the test holds the two probes firmly, one in each hand. In Figure 101 the base current to T1 flows through VR1 and R1 to Probe 1, then through the person's body to the Probe 2, and finally to the base of T1. The size of the collector current depends on the size of the base current, and this depends on how easily the current can flow through the subject. The size of the collector current is also determined by the setting of VR1. This is adjusted so that the voltage at point A is a few millivolts above zero. Note that this project is battery-powered and that all voltages and currents are small; there is no danger to the subject.

The voltage at A is compared with zero voltage by IC1, an operational amplifier which here is being used as a comparator. If the voltage at A is more than 0V, the output of the ic is less than 0V. When the subject tells a lie, sweating increases, more current flows between the probes, the collector current increases and the voltage at point A falls. As soon as it falls below 0V, the output of the amplifier swings sharply positive. Since the amplifier has very high gain, a few millivolts fall at

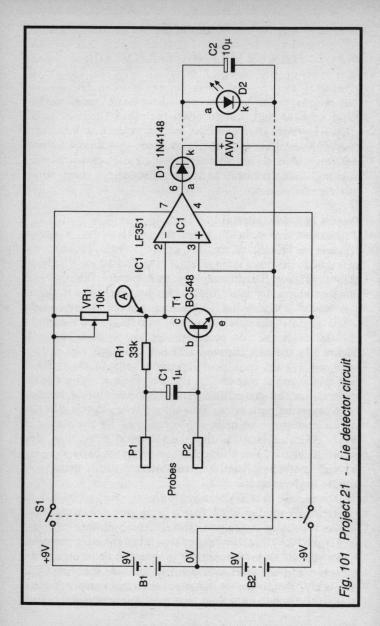

Fig. 101 Project 21 -- Lie detector circuit

A produces a rise of several volts at the output. The increased sweating needed to have this effect is very small, too small to be noticed except by its effect on the output of IC1. When the output of IC1 swings high (about 7V), current flows through D1 and this makes the audible warning device start to buzz. As an option, a flashing LED (D2) is connected in parallel with the AWD and this starts to flash.

The procedure is to ask the subject to hold the probes firmly and not to change the tightness of their grip. Adjust VR1 until the AWD *just* stops sounding. Then ask the subject an awkward or embarrassing question. Whether the buzzer sounds or not depends a lot on the state of mind of the subject. Some people are more responsive than others. But whatever happens, this circuit can create a lot of fun, especially at a party.

Component notes: The probes are two pieces of copper or aluminium tubing, about 10mm diameter and 120mm long. Wrap the stripped end of a flexible copper wire round one end of each tube. If the tube is copper, the wire can be soldered to the tube. If not, secure it by wrapping insulating tape or adhesive tape around the wired end. S1 is a double pole single throw (DPST) switch, but you may omit this and simply connect or disconnect the battery. D2 is a *flashing LED*; do not use an ordinary LED. The audible warning device is an 'electronic buzzer'.

Planning: There is scope for making the apparatus look very impressive, so as to intimidate the subject. Build it in a large case, decorated with metal foil panels, and painted in striking colours. Mount the LED on the front. The AWD must be secured firmly to the front panel; if the panel is large and thin, a really loud noise will be produced. Provide a large showy knob for VR1, and surround it with a striking (although meaningless) set of graduation marks and symbols. You could also add other lamps and LEDs, powered by another battery, to complete the effect. On the other hand, you may want to give the project a more serious 'medical' look; the case can be smaller, and more sober in colours, and have a large 'centre-zero' milliammeter in place of the AWD. If you do this, replace D1 with a resistor (about 4.7kΩ, depending on the meter) to restrict the meter current to a suitable level. The circuit requires a dual power supply of ±9V. This is most conveniently obtained by using two PP3 9V batteries with battery clips to make the connections. The circuit requires only a small amount of power, so the batteries should last for a reasonable time.

Stripboard layout:
Size: Standard.
Cuts: J15, G22–K22.
Links: A28–H28.
Resistors: R1 (D9–H9).
Pins: +9V (A3), 0V (J16), –9V (K3), VR1a/w (A13), VR1b (H13), P1 (D4), P2 (J6), AWD+ and D2a (C35).
Capacitors: C1+ (D7), C1– (J7), C2+ (C19), C2– (J19) C2 is not required if D2 not installed.
Semis: T1c (H11), T1b (J11), T1e (K11), D1a (J26), D1k (C26).
ICs: IC1 (G21).
Off-board: B1– to B2+ to 0V pin. B1+ to S1 (optional) to V+ pin. B2– to S1 (optional) to V– pin. Probe 1 to P1 pin and Probe 2 to P2 pin, using long flexible leads. Pin at C35 to AWD+ and D2a (optional). AWD– and D2k to 0V pin.

PCB design: Note the *three* power connections, +V, 0V and –V, wired to the batteries as described above.

Panel mounting: VR1, AWD, with optional D2 and S1.

Testing: Ask someone to hold the probes firmly, one in each hand, connect a voltmeter to point A, then adjust VR1. It should be possible to bring the voltage to zero at point A.

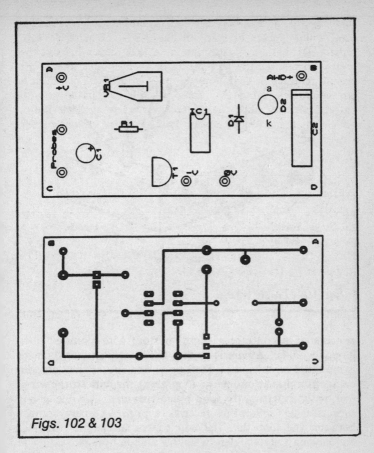

Figs. 102 & 103

Then turning the knob one way will make the AWD sound and the LED flash; the output voltage at pin 6 of IC1 will be about +8V. Turning the knob the other way makes the voltage swing to about −8V, silencing the AWD and stopping the flashing.

PCB assembly details are shown in Figures 102 and 103.

Project 22 − Twisty Wire

This is an updated version of the popular diversion often used as a fund-raiser at fetes and parties. The apparatus

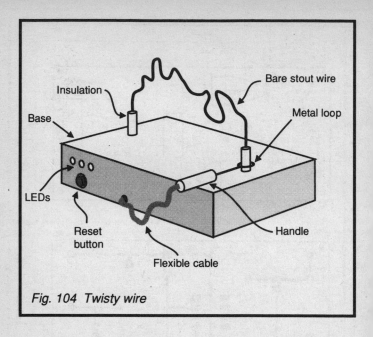

Fig. 104 Twisty wire

consists of a contorted length of stout wire mounted on a base (Fig.104). A wire loop that fits loosely around the wire is mounted on a handle. Starting at one end of the wire, the competitor has to move the loop along the wire to the other end, without letting the loop touch the wire. Anyone who is successful in doing this receives a prize. Usually contact between the loop and the wire makes an electric bell ring, announcing failure. Here we allow competitors two contacts before they are failed. On the first contact, a green LED begins to flash, meaning 'Go on!'. On the second contact a yellow LED flashes, indicating 'Take care'. On the third contact both LEDs flash and a third, red, LED comes on; at the same time a buzzer sounds. This indicates failure. If you like, you can award small prizes to those who manage to reach the other end of the wire with only one or two contacts registered.

The circuit (Fig.105) is based on a counter made from two J-K flip-flops (IC2). These are reset by pressing button S3,

144

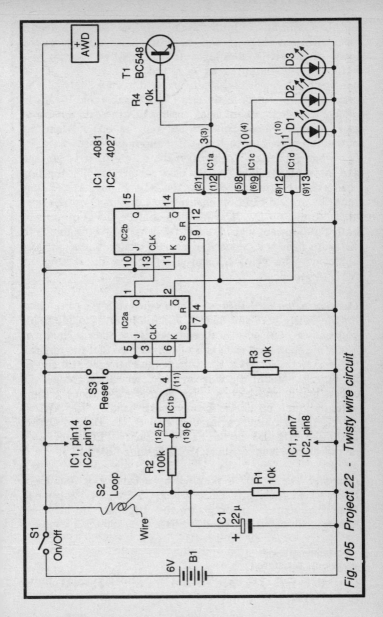

Fig. 105 Project 22 - Twisty wire circuit

145

and the $\overline{Q}$ outputs of both flip-flops go low. When contact is made between the wire and the loop (S2 in the figure) the input of gate IC1b goes high. It is an AND gate, acting as a buffer, so its output goes high too. R1 and C1 act to debounce S2; when contact is made, it is very likely that in practice there will be a dozen or more makes and breaks in rapid succession. Debouncing ensures that these do not count as a dozen or more contacts but only as one. When the output of IC1b goes high, the first flip-flop changes state; its $\overline{Q}$ output goes high. This makes the output of IC1d go high and D1 starts flashing. At the next contact, the first flip-flop changes state again; $\overline{Q}$ goes low and D1 goes out. At the same time the second flip-flop changes state and its $\overline{Q}$ output goes high, turning on D2. On the third contact, the $\overline{Q}$ outputs of both flip-flops are high; D1 and D2 light. Also both inputs to IC1a are high and, since it is an AND gate, its output goes high too. This lights D3 and also turns on T1, causing the AWD to sound.

Component notes: Use stout copper wire (16 SWG, or thicker) for the twisty wire and bend it in smooth curves to any shape you choose, but with both ends vertical. Slide a length of insulating tubing on each end of the wire, so that the ring can not make contact with the wire at the beginning and end of its journey. Mount the wire on a box, which will contain the circuit board, and battery. The loop is made from the same wire, mounted on a plastic or wooden handle. The AWD is an 'electronic buzzer' as used in Project 21. D1 and D2 are flashing LEDs; D3 could be an ordinary LED, preferably jumbo-sized (10mm diameter), or a flashing LED.

Planning: The circuit is powered by a battery of four C- or D-sized cells, held in a battery box. Switch S1 is optional. Note that some connections on the stripboard are made by leaving strips uncut, especially at C16, C21, and G27.

Stripboard layout:
Size: Standard.
Cuts: B11, H13, J13, B16, D16–H16, B21, D21–H21, B27–F27, H27, J27.

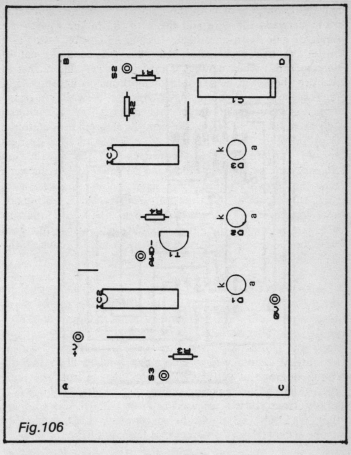

Fig.106

Links: B13–H19, E14–D23, H20–D32, E23–K23, A24–
F24, H24–J30, B25–E30, F31–K31.

Resistors: R1 (B6–K6), R2 (B9–F9), R3 (J34–K34), R4
(D12–J12).

Pins: +V (A3), 0V (K3), AWD– (H3), D1a (E20), D2a (F19),
D3a (D11), S2 loop (B7), S3 (J36).

Capacitors: C1+ (B8), C1– (K8).

Semis: T1c (H10), T1b (J10), T1e (K10).

ICs: IC1 (B15), IC2 (B26).

147

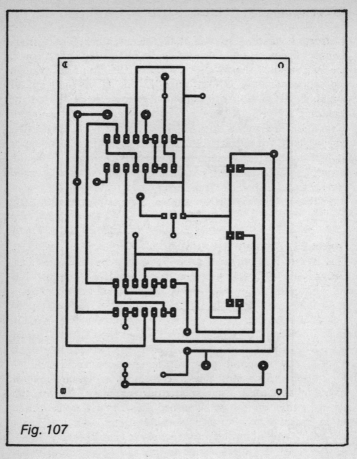

Fig. 107

Blobs: F15–G15, H15–J15, A18–B18, C18–D18, G18–H18, F26–G26, J26–K26, A29–B29, G29–H29.

Off-board: B1+ to S1 (optional) to pin A3. B1– to pin K3. AWD– to pin H3; AWD+ to +V. D1a to pin E20; D1k to 0V. D2a to pin F19; D2k to 0V. D3a to pin D11; D3k to 0V. S3 between pin J36 and +V. S2 wire to pin A3.

PCB design: The pin connections of IC1 are not the same as those in the stripboard version. In Figure 105, the figures in brackets refer to the pcb.

148

Panel mounting: S1 (if fitted), S3, D1—D3, AWD.

Testing: It is best to complete the circuit before testing. Switch on power; one or more of the LEDs may light. Touch the loop against the wire several times; the lamps go through the sequence, only D1 on, only D2 on, all on (and buzzer sounds). If there is no sequential action, check the circuit including S2, R1, R2 and C1. If a single contact between loop and wire causes the LEDs to change state erratically, check that C1 is correctly soldered in. If there is a sequence of lighting but LEDs come on in the wrong order, check the wiring of IC2 (especially for hair-like connections between opposite pins due to track not being properly cut).

PCB assembly details are shown in Figures 106 and 107.

Project 23 — Spooky

This is a fun circuit and is the basis of many weird effects. Design your own spook and activate it with this circuit. Or buy one ready-made; they are often on sale at stationers and other stores, especially just before Hallowe'en. When the circuit (Fig.108a & b) is triggered it generates a loud wailing noise for about 10 seconds. At the same time a pair of LEDs (the eyes of the spook) flash menacingly. The circuit can be triggered by a simple push-button, or with some kind of booby-trap. This may take the form of a pressure mat or magnetic switch, as used in security systems. Or you can arrange a microswitch to be turned on when a door is opened or an object is moved. The sound-triggered switch (Project 27) will switch on the spook whenever it detects a noise.

The timer IC1 gives a high output for approximately 10s when it is triggered. This high output supplies power to the rest of the circuit. The LEDs D1 and D2 are special flashing LEDs which have a built-in oscillator to make the LEDs flash about once a second. IC2 generates a short pulse every half-second. The pulse charges C4, but the charge leaks away through R6 between pulses. In this way the voltage at pin 9 of IC3 rises sharply every half-second, then falls gradually. IC3 is a voltage controlled oscillator and the changing voltage at pin 9 produces a pulsing wailing sound from the loudspeaker.

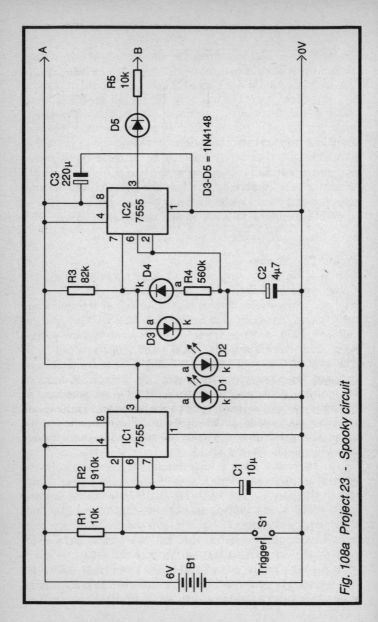

Fig. 108a Project 23 - Spooky circuit

150

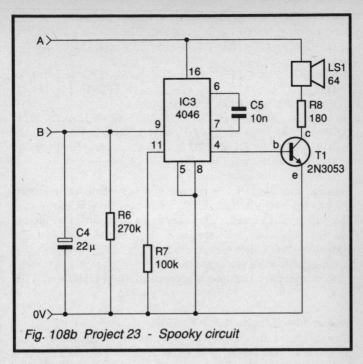

Fig. 108b Project 23 - Spooky circuit

Planning: Decide on the shape and size of the spook and of what materials it is to be constructed. Decide whether the circuit board and battery are to be contained within the spook or concealed elsewhere. Wiring from the trigger switch to the spook will have to be concealed, unless you intend to operate the spook only in darkness.

Stripboard layout:

Size: Standard.

Cuts: B8–E8, A12–E12, B18–E18, F21, B25–E25, G25, J25, D30, B30, B33–J33.

Links: A4–E4, D5–A13, B6–K6, C14–D21, A15–E15, B16–K16, F20–J36, F31–K31.

Resistors: R1 (A5–C5), R2 (A11–C11), R3 (A21–C21), R4 (D23–G23), R5 (F14–J14), R6 (F19–K19), R7 (G37–K37), R8 (B27–D27).

151

Pins: +V (A3), 0V (K3), S1 (C3), D1a/D2a (A14), LS1 (B26).
Capacitors: C1+ (D11), C1− (K11), C2+ (C15), C2− (K15), C3+ (B22), C3− (B14), C4+ (F17), C4− (K17), C5 (H25−G28).
Semis: D3a (C22), D3k (D22), D4a (G24), D4k (C24), D5a (D13), D5k (J13), T1c (D28), T1b (E29), T1e (F28).
ICs: IC1 (B7), IC2 (B17), IC3 (B32).
Blobs: A10−B10, C10−D10, A20−B20, J32−K32, A35−B35.
Off-board: Battery+ to pin A3; battery− to pin K3. S1 from 0V to pin C3. D1 and D2 anodes to pin A14; cathodes to 0V. LS1 to +V and pin B26.

Testing: Pin 3 of IC1 goes high for 10s when S1 is briefly closed; D1 and D2 flash for the same period and the rest of the circuit is activated. The effects can be modified by changing the values of R2 (length of 'on' period), R3 and R4 (pulsation rate), R6 (range of warbling pitch changes), R7 (average pitch), R8 (loudness).

PCB assembly details are shown in Figures 109 and 110.

Project 24 – Remote Robot Control

This project allows a relay to be switched on remotely, using an infra-red controller. It is sensitive up to a range of about 4 metres. It responds to the signal from an ordinary TV/Video remote controller, or you can make your own controller as described below. It has a toggle action, turning the relay on or off alternately each time the controller button is pressed. The relay is used to switch on any electrically powered device such as a lamp, an electric buzzer or bell, an electric motor or a solenoid. In this way, it can become the basis for controlling one action of a home-made robot. With a little ingenuity at designing simple logic circuits you could make it control several different actions in sequence.

When D1 (Fig.111) receives a pulse of infra-red, its leakage current increases and this is detected by the amplifier of IC1. The output goes low, triggering IC2 to produce a high pulse about 0.5s long. The LED D2 comes on, indicating that the signal has been received. IC3 contains two J-K flip-flops of which one is used to turn T1 (and the relay) on and off. Each

152

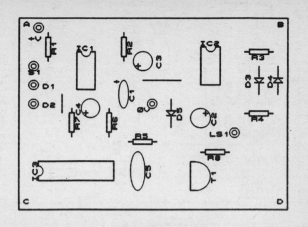

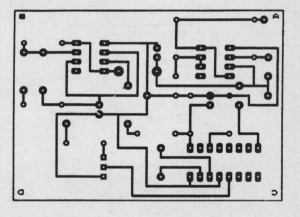

Figs. 109 & 110

153

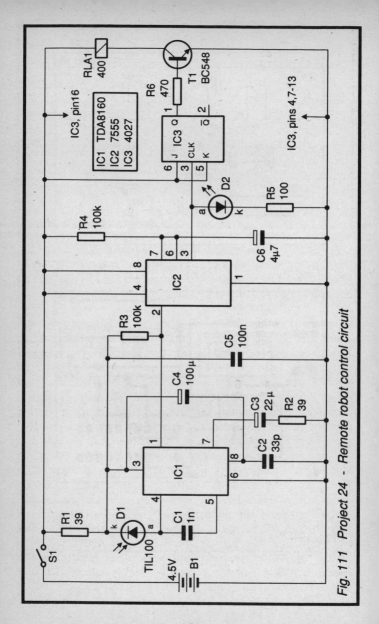

Fig. 111 Project 24 - Remote robot control circuit

154

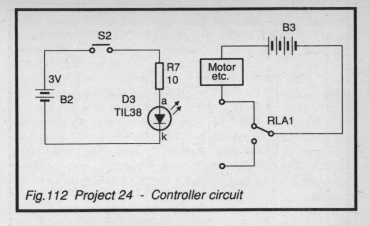

Fig.112 Project 24 - Controller circuit

time the voltage from pin 3 of IC2 goes high and D2 comes on, the flip-flop changes state. Its Q output changes from high to low or from low to high. The controller (Fig.112) consists of an infra-red LED which is switched on by pressing S2.

Component notes: D1 is an infra-red receiver diode (high speed PIN photodiode) and D2 is a high power infra-red LED. Any similar types can be used, but *miniature* IR receivers and emitters are usually unsuitable as they are not intended to operate at distances greater than a few millimetres. The relay is one designed for operating on 6V. A wide range of types is available, from sub-miniature relays (intended for mounting directly on the stripboard) to larger relays that require mounting on a separate board. Relays sometimes have a single pair of contacts which are either normally open or normally closed. More often a relay has changeover contacts, as in Figure 112. This makes it possible to control two devices, switching on either one or the other. Before purchasing a relay, check that its contacts have the required switching action and are rated to withstand the voltage and current for its intended use. The coil resistance specified in the diagram is 400Ω, which is typical of 6V relays, but coils with other resistances will almost certainly operate correctly in this circuit. C1 is a polystyrene capacitor, capacity 1nF (= 1000pF).

155

Planning: The unit may be housed in a small plastic case; mount the board so that D1 is close behind an aperture cut in the side of the case. Alternatively, mount D1 off-board, glued into the aperture, and connect it to the board by flexible leads. The circuit requires 40mA, so it needs a battery of *three* type C or D cells. The enclosure should be large enough to hold this. Note that this circuit operates on 4.5V, not 6V, as IC1 requires 4–5.25V. Any small enclosure is suitable for the controller; mount the board so that D3 is close behind an aperture cut in the front end of the case. The circuit takes 100mA for the short periods it is switched on; for most applications, a battery of *two* AA or AAA cells lasts for many months.

With D1 mounted as listed in the stripboard layout or as shown on the pcb design, if the diode is one of the commonest types, it is most sensitive when the IR reaches it from the right. Solder the very ends of its wire leads to the board, so that the package is well above the board. Then it can be turned in any direction (even to face left) by simply bending the wires; check that the two wires do not come into contact when bent.

BUILDING THE CONTROLLER (optional)

Stripboard layout:
Size: 10 strips by 10 holes, or almost any small scrap.
Resistor: R7 (A7–F7).
Pins: +V (A3), 0V (K3).
Semis: D3a (F10), D3k (K10); bend leads if necessary to direct beam.
Off-board: Battery positive to S2 to pin A3; battery negative to pin K3.

Panel mounting: S2 mounted where it can easily be pressed with a thumb when the case is hand held. Aperture D3.

Testing: In the dark, the LED is seen to glow dull red when the button is pressed.

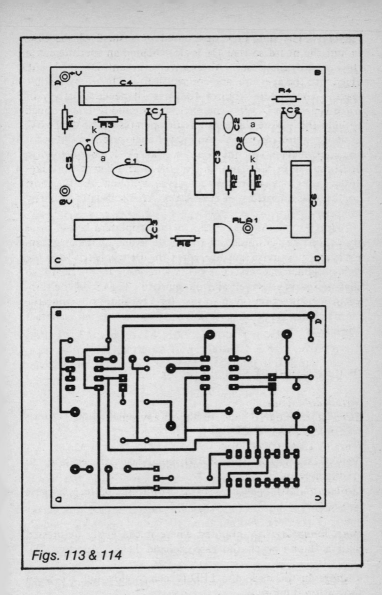

Figs. 113 & 114

157

BUILDING THE MAIN UNIT

Stripboard layout:

Size: Standard.

Cuts: C12–F12, C19–F19, J19, C23–F23, C29–H29, H32, B34–G34.

Links: C6–D21, E15–K15, C20–K20, E21–D30, F21–C27, A26–C26, A30–F30, G28–B30, E32–J32.

Resistors: R1 (A8–E8), R2 (J18–K18), R3 (C7–E7), R4 (A28–D28), R5 (H30–K30), R6 (G26–J26).

Pins: +V (A3), 0V (K3), RLA1 (H21).

Capacitors: C1 (F10–F15), C2 (C16–K16), C3+ (D17), C3– (J17), C4+ (E9), C4– (C15), C5 (E6–K6), C6+ (D26), C6– (K26).

Semis: D1a (any hole from F1 to F4), D1k (any hole from E1 to E4), D2a (D31), D2k (H31), T1c (H24), T1b (J24), T1e (K24).

ICs: IC1 (C11), IC2 (C22), IC3 (B33).

Blobs: D25–E25, F33–G33, H33–J33–K33, A36–B36, E36–F36–G36–H36–J36.

Off-board: Battery positive to S1; S1 to pin A3. Battery negative to K3. Battery positive to RLA1, other relay coil terminal to pin H21. Optional, mount D2 on panel and wire to D31 and H31.

Panel mounting: S1, terminals or sockets wired to relay contacts (Fig.112), aperture for D1.

Testing: Build and test the controller first, or use an ordinary TV/VCR/Stereo controller. Measure output from IC1, pin 1, which should be close to 4.5V. Direct the controller at D1 and press the button (any signalling button on a commercially made controller). Output from IC1 (pin 1) goes low, and D2 flashes. Wire a temporary circuit using the relay contacts, as in Figure 112 (for example a battery and a lamp). The lamp goes on or off each time the controller button is pressed.

PCB assembly details are shown in Figures 113 and 114 and the controller in Figures 115 and 116.

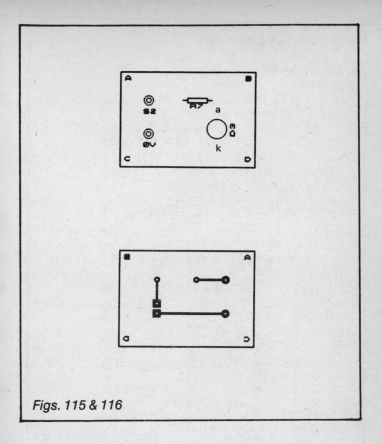

Figs. 115 & 116

Project 25 – Mini Organ

This is a simple 8-key organ, with a range of two octaves. The source of sound is IC1 (Fig.117), which is a voltage-controlled oscillator. Its output switches T1 on and off at audio frequencies. The output of IC1 is a square wave, but the sound is modified by R11 and C4 acting as a low-pass filter. This removes much of the 'edge' from the note, giving a pleasanter sound. The range of input voltages required to produce the 8 notes of an octave is provided by 8 potential dividers, each comprising a preset variable resistor and a 470kΩ fixed resistor.

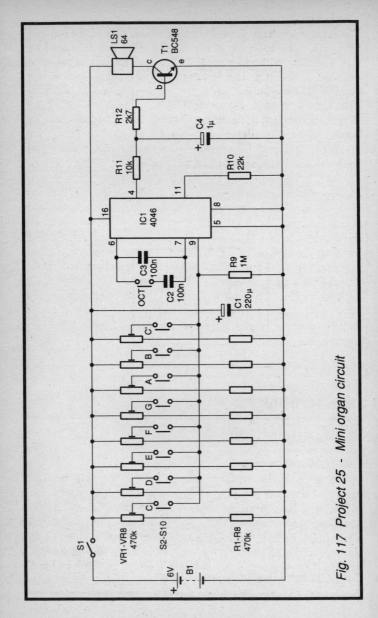

Fig. 117 Project 25 - Mini organ circuit

The required voltage is selected by pressing one of the buttons S2 to S9. The basic frequency of the VCO is determined by R10 and C3. With these values VR1 to VR8 can be tuned to produce notes of a few hundred hertz, ranging from a few octaves below middle C to a few octaves above it. Pressing S10 puts a second capacitor C2 in parallel with C3; this causes the frequency to drop to exactly half, giving a note one octave lower. If the presets are tuned to give notes one middle C to top C for example, pressing S10 produces notes from the octave below middle C.

Component notes: The 'keys' can be ordinary push-buttons (push-to-close type) but 'computer keys' have a rather lighter action, making the organ easier to play. If preferred, push-button S10 could be a push-to-open button, in which case pressing the button *raises* the pitch by one octave. Another approach is to use a stylus. Figure 118 shows 8 large brass drawing-pins as the contacts. These are wired to the wipers of VR1–VR8. The stylus consists of a wander plug, joined by a flexible wire to the junction between R9 and IC1, pin 9. Touch the stylus against any drawing pin and the corresponding note is heard.

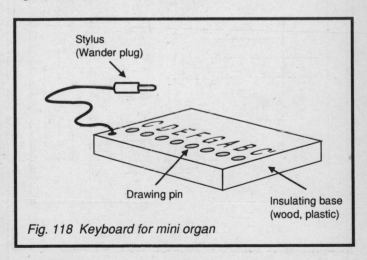

Fig. 118 Keyboard for mini organ

Planning: The project takes about 40mA, so a battery of four type D cells is required. The keys or drawing-pin contacts are mounted on top of the enclosure, or on a base as in Figure 118. The average pitch may be decreased by reducing R10. The sound may be made more mellow by increasing C4. To reduce volume, wire a resistor (47Ω to 150Ω) between LS1 and the +V line.

Stripboard layout:

Size: 16 strips (A to Q) by 39 holes, but could be build on two standard boards.

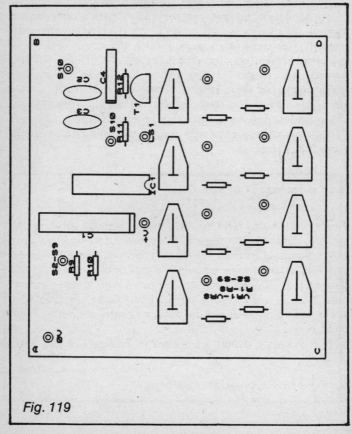

Fig. 119

Cuts: H10, B12, C12, E12, F12, B21, C21, E21, F21, J23, B30, C30, E30, F30, H19–P19, M23, O28, P28.

Links: A11–G11, D9–Q9, L17–J24, M17–Q17.

Resistors: R1 (C7–D7), R2 (C16–D16), R3 (C25–D25), R4 (C34–D34), R5 (D8–E8), R6 (D17–E17), R7 (D26–E26), R8 (D35–E35), R9 (P23–Q23), R10 (N22–Q22), R11 (J25–M25), R12 (M30–P30), VR1 (A4, C4, B8), VR2 (A13, C13, B17), VR3 (A22, C22, B26), VR4 (A31, C31, B35), VR5 (E4, G4, F8), VR6 (E13, G13, F17), VR7 (E22, G22, F26), VR8 (E31, G31, F35).

Pins: +V (A3), 0V (Q3), S2 (B10), S3 (B19), S4 (B28), S5 (B36), S6 (F10), S7 (F19), S8 (F28), S9 (F36), S10 (H6 and N6), S2 to S9 (P27), LS1 (O36).

Capacitors: C1+ (A20), C1– (D20), C2 (H8–O8), C3 (O10–N16), C4+ (M24), C4– (Q24).

Semis: T1c (O32), T1b (P32), T1e (Q32).

ICs: IC1 (H18).

Blobs: P18–Q18, G21–H21.

Off-board: Battery positive to S1; S1 to pin A3; battery negative to Q3. One terminal of S2–S9 to pins S2–S9; other terminal of S2–S9 all to pin P27. S10 to pins H6 and N6. LS1 to +V and pin O36.

Panel mounting: S1 to S10, LS1.

Testing: Wipers to VR1 to VR8 are at voltages between 3V and 6V, depending on setting. Press each of S2 to S9 in turn; a different note is heard for each. Press and hold S2 to S9 in turn and adjust the corresponding preset until each produces a note of the required pitch, as compared with another instrument such as a piano, or a set of tuning forks. Pressing S10 at the same time as any other one key causes the pitch to fall by an octave.

PCB assembly details are shown in Figures 119 and 120.

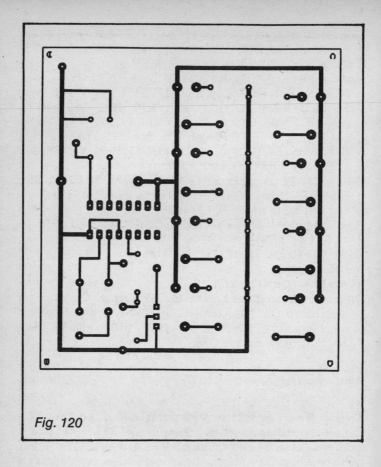

Fig. 120

Project 26 – Nail and Cable Detector
Hammering in a picture-hook may be a dangerous operation if
there is a live mains cable hidden below the wall plaster. It
can lead to an unpleasant, if not lethal, electric shock and
may also blow the house fuse. Less dangerous, but irritating,
is trying to hammer in a nail or insert a screw and finding that
its entry is blocked by another nail or some other metal object
below the surface. This device, whose circuit is shown in
Figure 121, detects metallic objects at a distance up to 50mm.

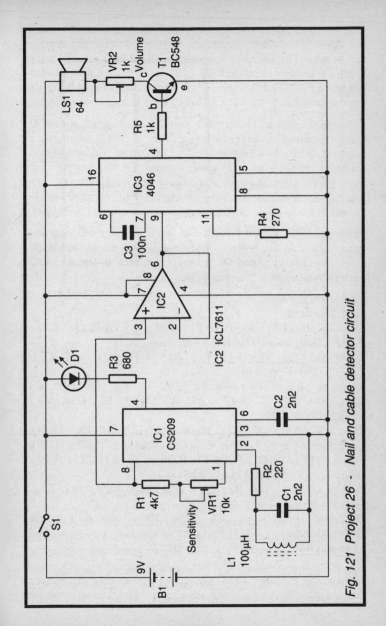

Fig. 121 Project 26 - Nail and cable detector circuit

165

It is sensitive to ferromagnetic metals such as iron and steel, and also to non-ferrous metals such as aluminium, copper and brass. The detector normally emits a high-pitched note from its loudspeaker, and its LED is out. As it is moved toward a metal object the pitch begins to fall, reaching its lowest (and turning on the LED) when it is nearest the object.

Component notes: The sensing coil L1 consists of about 70 turns of enamelled copper wire (approx. 28 SWG) wound on a piece of ferrite rod (aerial rod) about 25mm long and 8mm diameter. Wrap a piece of paper around the rod first and fix with sticky tape; then wind on the turns irregularly so that they cross each other, forming a compact 'ball'. A ready-made alternative is a small choke, inductance approximately $100\mu H$.

Planning: Both the stripboard and the pcb design are long and narrow so that the project can be housed in one of the plastic cases specially intended for probes. It works on 9V so a PP3 battery is a suitably compact power source.

Stripboard layout:
Size: Standard.
Cuts: D7, F7, H7, E10–H10, F14, C15, D15, C18–J18, B23–F23, E28, B30–D30, B32–J32.
Links: G6–K6, A13–F13, F15–K15, D16–E21, A21–C21, E22–J35, F30–J30.
Resistors: R1 (C14–E14), R2 (F6–F8), R3 (D8–H8), R4 (G36–K36), R5 (E27–E29), VR1 (C7, E7, D3), VR2 (B25, D25, C29).
Pins: +V (A3), 0V (K3), probe L1 (F3, H3), LS1 (B24).
Capacitors; C1 (F5–H5), C2 (G14–K14), C3 (H23–G29).
Semis: D1a (A9), D1k (D9), T1c (D24), T1b (E24), T1e (F24).
ICs: IC1 (E9), IC2 (C17), IC3 (B31).
Blobs: C3–D3, G3–H3, C20–D20, B29–C29, J31–K31, A34–B34.
Off-board: Battery positive to S1; S1 to pin A3; battery negative to pin K3. L1 to pins F3 and H3. LS1 to +V and to pin B24. Optionally mount D1 off-board.

Panel mounting: Mount L1 on the front end of the case. On the panel mount S1, LS1. Mount D1 on the panel, or on the board with an aperture cut in the case.

Testing: Hold the device so that the probe is 10cm or more from any metal object: the note is high and D1 is out. If the LED is on, adjust VR1 until it goes out. Adjust VR2 for suitable volume. Adjust VR1 so that the pitch of the note falls *slightly* below its highest level. Move the device toward a small (2.5cm) iron nail; the pitch falls further as the probe comes nearer to the nail. D1 comes on and the pitch falls to its lowest level when the nail is less than 4cm from the probe. It may be necessary to adjust VR1 finely to make the device sufficiently sensitive that the pitch begins to fall as soon as the probe is within 5cm of the metal. In general it is sensitive to larger objects at greater distances, but is less sensitive to non-ferrous metals (such as copper cables) than it is to ferrous metals. It detects cables whether or not they are carrying a current.

PCB assembly details are shown in Figures 122 and 123.

Project 27 — Sound-operated Switch

There are many applications for a circuit which supplies power when it has detected a noise. We originally designed this as a phone-bell repeater, to sound a loud siren outdoors when the phone rings indoors. As a clap switch, it can be used for remotely controlling a variety of devices, including switching on a low-voltage porch lamp when someone comes to the door at night. It can be used to switch on a small motor in a home-made robot. It is particularly sensitive to high-pitched whistling sounds, so there is the possibility of using it to control a model train by blowing a whistle. Another use for this circuit is as a baby-listener. When the baby cries upstairs, a lamp or small buzzer comes on in the living-room downstairs.

Sound is picked up by a microphone (MIC1, Fig.124), and the signal from the microphone is amplified by T1. C2 and R4 together act as a high-pass filter so that any mains interference is removed from the signal. The signal then goes to a diode pump (D1/D2) which causes a charge to build up on C3 when a sound is detected. The rising voltage causes T2 to produce a low-level pulse, which triggers the timer circuit based on IC1. The output of this ic goes high (for a length of time depending on R8 and C5), supplying power to an LED and an audible

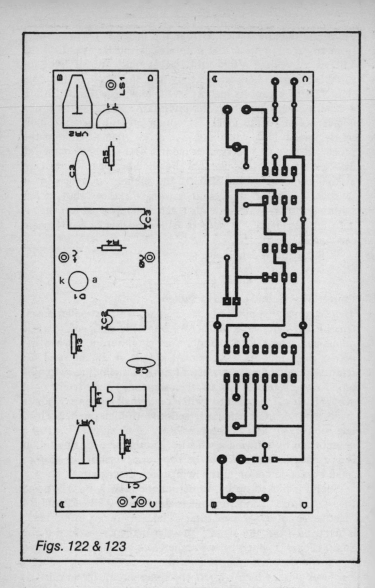

Figs. 122 & 123

168

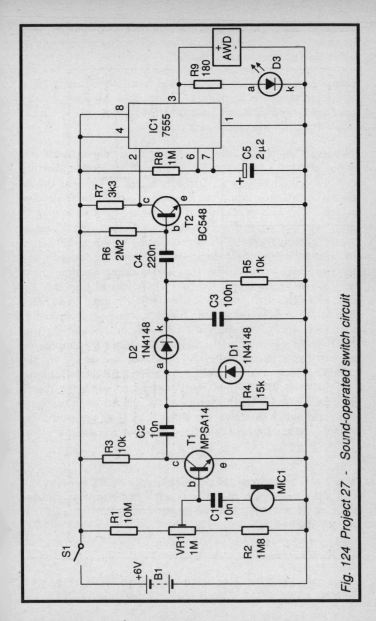

Fig. 124 Project 27 - Sound-operated switch circuit

169

warning device. It could also switch on a relay which could, in turn, be used to switch on low-voltage lamps, motors or other electrically-powered devices.

Component notes: MIC1 is a crystal 'microphone insert'. For VR1, use a *vertical* miniature trimpot. The AWD can be any solid-state siren or buzzer intended for running on 6V. In the pcb version, C5 has radial leads (p15).

Planning: The circuit runs on 6V and takes only 3mA when it is not actually powering the LED and AWD, so a small battery of four cells is adequate. Decide whether to have the microphone in the enclosure or to locate it externally on the end of a lead. The lead should not be more than about 1m long to avoid picking up mains interference. If it is 30cm long or more, it should preferably be connected to the circuit board by shielded cable. Also decide which device or devices are to be switched — the LED, the AWD, both, or some other device. IC1 can supply up to 100mA which is enough for several LEDs, and possibly two sirens, all wired in parallel. If a larger current is needed, connect a relay coil instead of the AWD (p.7). If you need only an audible warning, the LED is not essential. It is helpful to install it, temporarily at least, as a useful indicator when you are setting up the circuit. The lead to an AWD can be 10 or more metres long.

Finally decide on the length of time for which the switch is to be active. With the values of R8 and C5 given in Figure 124, the switch is active for about 2.5s *after* the sound has ceased. Other times are calculated using the equation:

$$t = 1.1RC$$

where t is in seconds, R is the resistance of R8 in ohms and C is the capacitance of C5 in farads. The largest practicable value of R is 10MΩ and the largest practicable value of C is about 470μF.

Stripboard layout:
Size: Standard.
Cuts: D6, F6, D14–F14, B19, C19, E19, H19, D27, E27, B33–E33.

Links: F9–K9, E26–K26, B27–K27, A28–E28.

Resistors: R1 (A5–D5), R2 (F5–K5), R3 (A8–D8), R4 (B14–K14), R5 (F20–K20), R6 (A22–D22), R7 (A26–C26), R8 (A37–C37), R9 (D30–H30), VR1 (D3, E4, F3).

Pins: +V (A3), 0V (K3), MIC1 (J6), AWD+ (D29), AWD– (K29).

Capacitors: C1 (E8–J8), C2 (B13–D13), C3 (F18–K18), C4 (D17–F23), C5+ (D37), C5– (K37).

Semis: D1a (K15), D1k (B15), D2a (F16), D2k (B16), D3a (H32), D3k (K32), T1c (D11), T1b (E11), T1e (F11), T2c (C24), T2b (D24), T2e (E24).

ICs: IC1 (B32).

Blobs: A35–B35, C35–D35.

Off-board: B1 with negative terminal wired to 0V pin and positive terminal to S1. Other terminal of S1 goes to +V pin. MIC1 cable shield (if shielded cable used) to 0V pin, and to the metal case of the microphone at the other end (if case is metal). Cable core connects the other terminal of the microphone to the pin at J6. With unshielded cable, connect to 0V and J6. It is better not to connect the AWD until the circuit has been tested. The LED can be mounted off-board, through two pins at H32 and K32.

Testing: Apply power; the LED comes on for the specified period of time. If it does not come on, check that it is mounted the right way round. If it comes on permanently, measure the voltage at pin 2 of IC1, which should be close to 6V. If it is not, check the wiring and the connections of T2. You may need to reduce the value of R6 to 1.8MΩ, but this is unlikely. Connect a voltmeter to the collector of T1 (or the D8 wire of R3). Adjust VR1 until the voltage is 3V, or reasonably close, say between 2.5V and 3.5V. If the voltage stays close to 6V whatever the setting of VR1, check the wiring and soldering. If this appears to be correct, try substituting a resistor of higher value (say 2.2MΩ) for R2. If the voltage at T1 collector stays close to 0V, substitute a smaller resistor for R2.

PCB assembly details are shown in Figures 125 and 126.

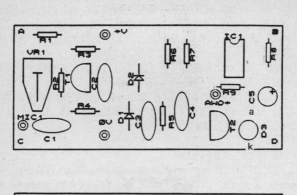

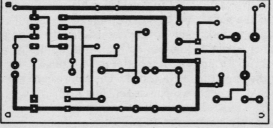

Figs. 125 & 126

Project 28 – Electronic Sculpture
This is not so much a project but a suggestion for a whole
range of projects that you could design and build. The circuit
itself is relatively simply, but it is the way that you build it
that counts. An electronic sculpture is a model figure built
up from electronic components. You have the task of finding
components with the right shapes and colours to make up a
three-dimensional sculpture of a human or of any other
animal you choose. Figure 127 shows an example of what we
mean. This friendly fellow has a body made from a PP3 battery,

172

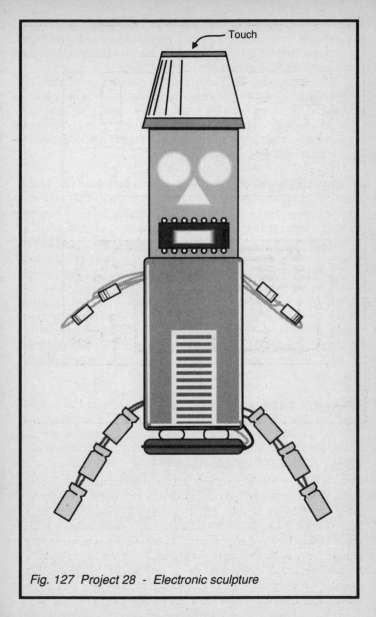

Touch

Fig. 127 Project 28 - Electronic sculpture

arms made from resistors, and legs made from electrolytic capacitors. His hat is a plastic control knob and, when you touch the top of his hat, the LEDs that are his eyes, nose and tongue flash for a period of about 2 minutes.

The circuit (Fig.128) comprises two timers, in one ic. The first timer is wired as a monostable with a pulse length of 2 minutes. It is triggered by touching the metal plate that is on top of the hat. Its output (pin 5) then goes high and is fed to pin 10, the reset input of the second timer. This enables the counter which then flashes the LEDs.

Component notes: Figure 127 is only an example of a possible sculpture. You may want to vary this design slightly or invent something entirely different. It is probably better to use the older, larger type of electrolytic capacitor, in preference to the newer miniature ones, since the older types are of a more suitable size for modelling. Similarly use large size resistors (2.5 watt or higher) rather than the small 0.25W, even though high-wattage resistors are not needed to carry the small currents of this circuit. The eyes are LEDs of the usual shape; they could be any colour but you might like to try the newer blue LEDs (even though they are expensive). The nose is a triangular shaped LED and the tongue is a rectangular LED. The ic makes a mouth with teeth, and you could paint this red, using artist's acrylic or oil paint.

Planning: Planning plays an important part in this project. Before assembling the components into the sculpture, lay them out on a sheet of paper to check that they are of suitable size, shape and colour. You can also plan to add extra touches made from other components which are not actually part of the circuit. Examples are spectacles made from cored solder or thick copper wire, a bow-tie made from brightly coloured insulating tape, ear-rings made from washers (make the ears from thin card, glued in place). There really is no end to what you can devise.

Stripboard layout: See Figure 129. The crosses indicate where the copper strips are cut. Note there is NO cut at F10. Mount the components first, keeping wire leads of capacitors, resistors

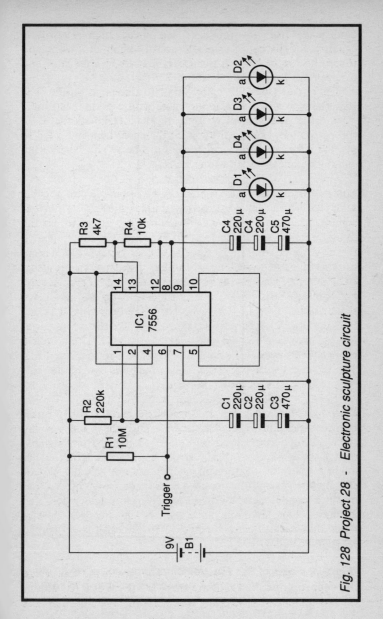

Fig. 128 Project 28 - Electronic sculpture circuit

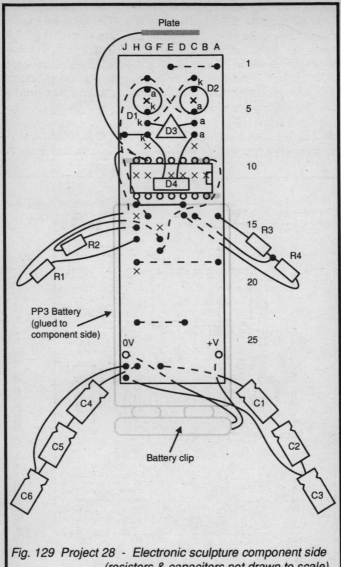

Fig. 129 Project 28 - Electronic sculpture component side
(resistors & capacitors not drawn to scale)

and LEDs long where necessary. D4 is on very long wires, bent to bring the LED in front of IC1. The wire links in this project are at the rear of the board, to keep them out of sight from the front, as indicated by the dashed lines. Terminal pins are soldered at A14, C14, D14, G14, H15, H16, A26, J26, F27, H27, J27 and J29 for the attachment of resistors, capacitors and the battery clip. The battery is fixed to the front of the board using a double-sided adhesive pad.

PCB design: See Figures 130 and 131. The capacitor sets are exchanged in this design, C1−C3 on the left, as seen from the

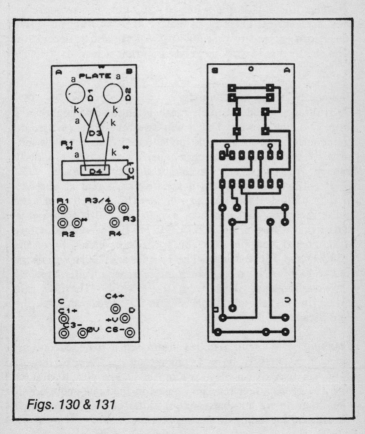

Figs. 130 & 131

front, and C4 – C6 on the right. There are 3 copper pads seen on the track side of the board; do not drill these. Their positions as seen from the component side are marked with an asterisk (*). The isolated pad near edge AB is for the touch-plate connection; also solder a wire link on the back (copper side) of the pcb from this pad to the pad for R1. The other end of R1 goes to the terminal pin labelled R1. R2 is soldered to the two terminal pins marked R2. One of these, indicated by *, is to be joined by a wire link to the pad (also marked *) which is joined to pins 1 and 2 of the ic.

Testing: Check that the wires to capacitors and resistors are not in electrical contact; insulating tape or PVC insulating sleeve can be used to prevent this, and can also be decorative. The circuit should work correctly first time it is tried.

Project 29 – Two-tone Sounder
A two-tone sound is much more attention-catching than a note of a single tone. This is why two-tone sirens are used on ambulances, fire-engines and police cars. This circuit is suitable for use as a door alert, a caller for an invalid or elderly person, or as part of any warning or security system.

IC1 (Fig.132) produces a square-wave signal at approximately 1500Hz. This goes to a divider (IC2) which divides the pulse rate by 2 and produces a signal at 750Hz from pin 9. The signal is further divided by 512, to give an approximately 1.5Hz signal from pin 14. This is used to switch between the 1500Hz and 750Hz tones. The 1500Hz and 750Hz signals are fed to two NAND gates, which are switched on alternately by the low-frequency signal from IC2 pin 14. The final gate mixes the signals and feeds this to T1, which activates the loudspeaker.

Planning: The circuit requires 40mA when switched on but, since it is likely to be powered intermittently, a battery of four AA or AAA cells lasts a long time. The push-button S1 and the loudspeaker may be housed in the same enclosure as the circuit board and battery, but either or both can be sited externally, depending on the application.

178

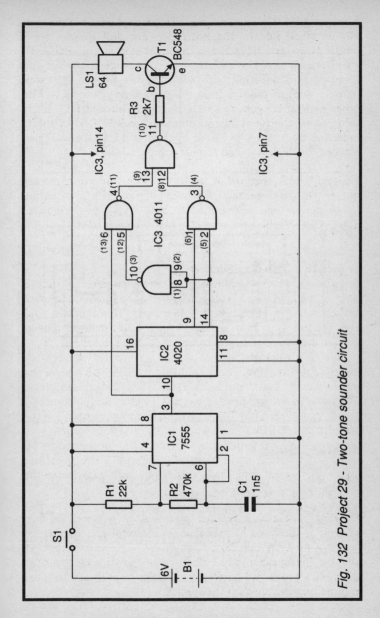

Fig. 132 Project 29 - Two-tone sounder circuit

179

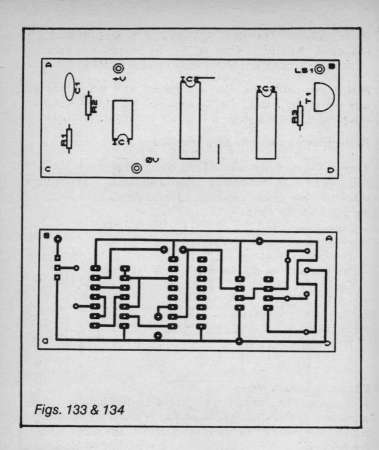

Figs. 133 & 134

Stripboard layout:

Size: Standard.

Cuts: B7–E7, B13–E13, B15–J15, B20, C20, E20–G20, J20, C24, D24, F24, H24, J24, H28, J28.

Links: A4–E4, C4–D10, D4–H18, B5–K5, J18–C21, G19–K19, F21–D27, A27–C27, D22–J27.

Resistors: R1 (A10–C10), R2 (C11–D11), R3 (F29–J29).

Pins: +V (A3), 0V (K3), LS1 (H34).

Capacitors: C1 (D12–K12).

Semis: T1c (H31), T1b (J31), T1e (K31).

ICs: IC1 (B6), IC2 (B14), IC3 (C23).

180

Blobs: A9–B9, J14–K14, A17–B17, J23–K23, H26–J26.

Off-board: Battery positive to S1. S1 to pin A3; battery negative to pin K3. LS1 between +V and pin H34.

PCB design: Note that IC1 is mounted with pin 1 toward side CD of the board. Pin numbers for IC3 are different in this version, and are given in brackets on the circuit diagram.

Panel mounting: S1 and LS1, both operational.

Testing: Connect one terminal of a crystal earphone to the 0V line and its other terminal to a 100nF capacitor. Touch the other terminal of the capacitor to these points in the circuit and listen for the signal:

High pitch (1500Hz) at IC1/3, IC2/10, IC3/6(13).

Intermittent high pitch at IC3/4(11), IC3/12(8).

Low pitch (750Hz) at IC2/9, IC3/1(6).

Intermittent low pitch at IC3/3(4), IC3/13(9).

Clicking at 2Hz at IC2/14, IC3/8(1), IC3/9(2), IC3/5(12), IC3/2(5).

Two-tone at IC3/11(10).

Pin numbers of IC3 in brackets refer to the pcb version. PCB assembly details are shown in Figures 133 and 134.

Project 30 – Party Meter

If the success of a party can be judged by the loudness of the music and the chattering, this project is a way of measuring it. In other words, this is a noise meter. Sound picked up by the microphone (Fig.135a & b) is converted into an electrical signal which is amplified by IC1a. IC1b, D1, C1 and R5 form a peak level circuit. As the output voltage of IC1b peaks in the positive direction, the charge on C1 peaks correspondingly. But, as the signal peaks in the negative direction, the one-way action of D1 prevents C1 from discharging. In noisy periods the charge on C1 builds up to a level determined by the loudest sound. The charge leaks away slowly through R5, so that in quiet periods lasting more than a few seconds, the charge becomes appreciably reduced; with longer quiet or silent periods, it leaks away almost completely. The voltage across C1 is detected by IC1c, connected as a voltage follower

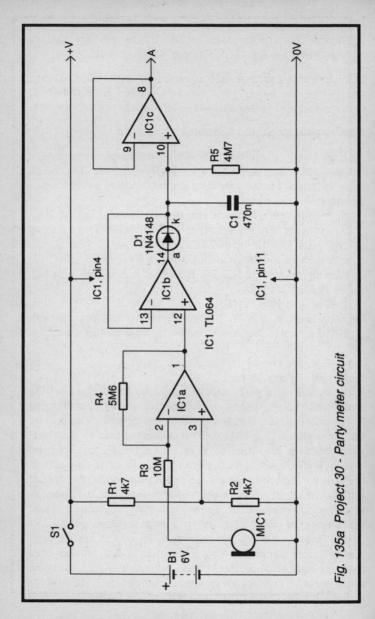

Fig. 135a Project 30 - Party meter circuit

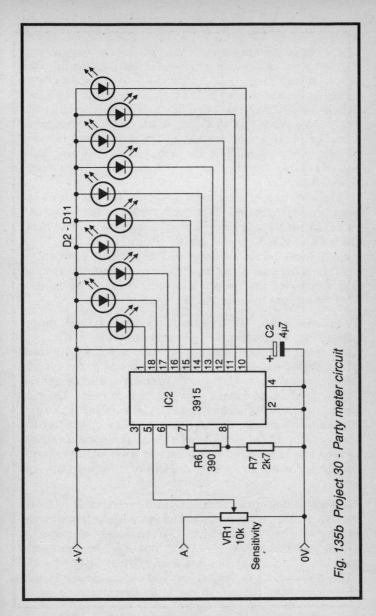

Fig. 135b Project 30 - Party meter circuit

and takes virtually no current from C1. Its output is exactly the same as the voltage on C1, and it is able to supply plenty of current to the next stage of the circuit. The output from IC1c goes to VR1, which acts as a sensitivity control. Part of the voltage from IC1c is tapped off by potential-divider action (p.29) and goes to IC2, which is a bargraph display ic. This is connected so that one LED is illuminated at any time, producing a moving spot of light. If the LEDs are arranged in a row (or in an arrangement as in the pcb version) the spot of light moves along from the 'low' end (D2) to the 'high' end (D11). As the party gets noisier, the spot of light moves from left to right.

The version of the bargraph ic chosen for this circuit has a logarithmic response. Each LED corresponds to a voltage twice that of the one below it on the scale. When D11 is lit, the noise level is 512 times greater than when D2 is lit. This scale is used because a noise that is twice as powerful as another noise sounds *less* than twice as powerful to the ear. The lighting of the lamps corresponds more closely to how loud we *perceive* the sound to be.

Component notes: MIC1 can be a crystal or dynamic microphone, or an inexpensive microphone insert. IC1 is a quadruple operational amplifier ic, from which we use three of the amplifiers. Choose the LEDs according to the type of display you prefer. They can be ordinary red LEDs but the display is more striking if you use high intensity LEDs or jumbo-sized (10mm diameter) LED. Or combine the two in super-bright jumbos. Consider the possibility of building the display with LEDs of different colours (for example, green for the low end, yellow for the middle range and red (Stop!) for the top end. You could use LEDs of different shapes, as well.

Planning: Power this circuit with four type C or D cells in a battery holder. It can be housed in a rectangular box with the display on the top panel, but there is plenty of scope for dressing up the project to make it look more impressive and partyish. The pcb version has a ready-made layout for the LEDs but you can use any layout you choose simply by running wires from the pcb to the LEDs mounted on a panel.

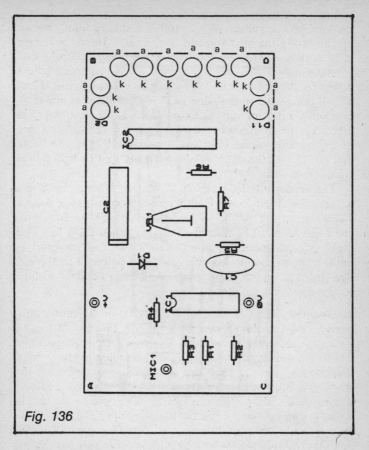

Fig. 136

Stripboard layout:

Size: Standard.

Cuts: G7, B12–H12, B19–G19, H21, A25, A29–J29.

Links: B6–D15, A10–E10, E15–K15, C17–F17, A23–C23, D24–K24, B25–D25.

Resistors: R1 (A9–E9), R2 (D8–K8), R3 (C6–G6), R4 (B8–C8), R5 (F18–K18), R6 (G26–H26), R7 (H25–K25).

Pins: +V (A3), 0V (K3), MIC1 (G3), VR1a (H20), VR1w (E20), D2k (A26), D3k (A33), D4k (B35), D5k (C33), D6k (D35), D7k (E33), D8k (F35), D9k (G33), D10k

185

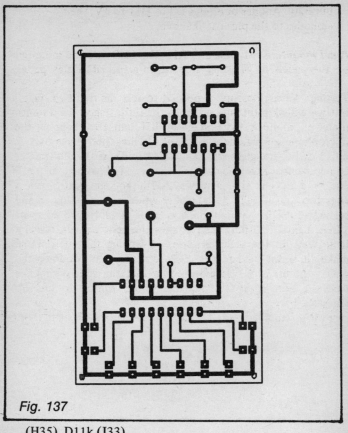

Fig. 137

(H35), D11k (J33).

Capacitors: C1 (F16–K16), C2+ (A22), C2– (K22).

Semis: D1a (B16), D1k (C16).

ICs: IC1 (B11), IC2 (A28).

Blobs: G14–H14, F28–G28.

Off-board: Battery positive to S1; S1 to pin A3; battery negative to pin K3. MIC1 to 0V and pin G3; use a short connection, preferably no more than 50mm. If the microphone has a metal case and one of its terminals is connected to this, this terminal should be the one connected to the 0V line. VR1 between pin H20 and 0V; its wiper to pin E20. Anodes of diodes D2 to D11 to +V; their cathodes to the pins listed above.

Panel mounting: S1, MIC1, VR1. The LEDs may be mounted on the panels of the enclosure or on a special display panel.

Testing: An oscilloscope is needed to test the first two stages, but we will skip this and go on to the third stage. Use a multimeter to monitor the voltage at IC1, pin 10. Tapping the microphone, or making a loud noise makes the voltage rise. It falls slowly, though it will fall more rapidly if the multimeter is a low-impedance moving-coil meter. The voltage at pin 8 rises and falls in the same way. The voltage at IC2, pin 5 rises too, but usually by a smaller amount, depending on the setting of VR1. One of the LEDs, or possibly two adjacent LEDs, lights. Turning VR1 makes the spot of light travel a little way up the scale; a noise, or tapping the microphone makes it travel further up. Silence makes it move down the scale. In use, VR1 is adjusted so that the spot of light is near the bottom of the scale, but moves almost to the top when the party is at its noisiest.

PCB assembly details are shown in Figures 136 and 137.

Appendix

NAMES AND ADDRESSES OF SUPPLIERS

The following two companies issue mail order catalogues of electronic components:

Cirkit Distribution Limited
Park Lane, Broxbourne,
Hertfordshire EN10 7NQ
England
(Tel: 0992 448899)

They supply the special pcb chemicals in dispenser packaging, as mentioned on page 55.

Maplin Electronics
P.O. Box 3, Rayleigh,
Essex SS6 8LR
England
(Tel: 0702 552911)

This company also has shops in many cities and larger towns.

Notes

Notes

Notes

Notes

Please note following is a list of other titles that are available in our range of Radio, Electronics and Computer books.

These should be available from all good Booksellers, Radio Component Dealers and Mail Order Companies.

However, should you experience difficulty in obtaining any title in your area, then please write directly to the Publisher enclosing payment to cover the cost of the book plus adequate postage.

If you would like a complete catalogue of our entire range of Radio, Electronics and Computer Books then please send a Stamped Addressed Envelope to:

BERNARD BABANI (publishing) LTD
THE GRAMPIANS
SHEPHERDS BUSH ROAD
LONDON W6 7NF
ENGLAND

160	Coil Design and Construction Manual	£2.50
227	Beginners Guide to Building Electronic Projects	£1.95
BP28	Resistor Selection Handbook	£0.60
BP36	50 Circuits Using Germanium Silicon & Zener Diodes	£1.95
BP37	50 Projects Using Relays, SCRs and TRIACs	£2.95
BP39	50 (FET) Field Effect Transistor Projects	£2.95
BP42	50 Simple LED Circuits	£1.95
BP44	IC 555 Projects	£2.95
BP48	Electronic Projects for Beginners	£1.95
BP49	Popular Electronic Projects	£2.50
BP53	Practical Electronics Calculations & Formulae	£3.95
BP56	Electronic Security Devices	£2.95
BP74	Electronic Music Projects	£2.95
BP76	Power Supply Projects	£2.50
BP78	Practical Computer Experiments	£1.75
BP80	Popular Electronic Circuits – Book 1	£2.95
BP84	Digital IC Projects	£1.95
BP85	International Transistor Equivalents Guide	£3.95
BP87	50 Simple LED Circuits – Book 2	£1.95
BP88	How to Use Op-amps	£2.95
BP90	Audio Projects	£2.50
BP92	Electronics Simplified – Crystal Set Construction	£1.75
BP94	Electronic Projects for Cars and Boats	£1.95
BP95	Model Railway Projects	£2.95
BP97	IC Projects for Beginners	£1.95
BP98	Popular Electronic Circuits – Book 2	£2.95
BP99	Mini-matrix Board Projects	£2.50
BP105	Aerial Projects	£2.50
BP107	30 Solderless Breadboard Projects – Book 1	£2.95
BP110	How to Get Your Electronic Projects Working	£2.95
BP111	Audio	£3.95
BP115	The Pre-computer Book	£1.95
BP118	Practical Electronic Building Blocks – Book 2	£1.95
BP121	How to Design and Make Your Own PCB's	£2.50
BP122	Audio Amplifier Construction	£2.95
BP125	25 Simple Amateur Band Aerials	£1.95
BP126	BASIC & PASCAL in Parallel	£1.50
BP130	Micro Interfacing Circuits – Book 1	£2.75
BP131	Micro Interfacing Circuits – Book 2	£2.75
BP132	25 Simple SW Broadcast Band Aerials	£1.95
BP136	25 Simple Indoor and Window Aerials	£1.75
BP137	BASIC & FORTRAN in Parallel	£1.95
BP138	BASIC & FORTH in Parallel	£1.95
BP144	Further Practical Electronics Calculations & Formulae	£4.95
BP145	25 Simple Tropical and MW Band Aerials	£1.75
BP146	The Pre-BASIC Book	£2.95
BP147	An Introduction to 6502 Machine Code	£2.95
BP148	Computer Terminology Explained	£1.95
BP171	Easy Add-on Projects for Amstrad CPC 464, 664, 6128 & MSX Computers	£2.95
BP176	A TV-DXers Handbook (Revised Edition)	£5.95
BP177	An Introduction to Computer Communications	£2.95
BP179	Electronic Circuits for the Computer Control of Robots	£2.95
BP182	MIDI Projects	£2.95
BP184	An Introduction to 68000 Assembly Language	£2.95
BP187	A Practical Reference Guide to Word Processing on the Amstrad PCW8256 & PCW8512	£5.95
BP190	More Advanced Electronic Security Projects	£2.95
BP192	More Advanced Power Supply Projects	£2.95
BP193	LOGO for Beginners	£2.95
BP196	BASIC & LOGO in Parallel	£2.95
BP197	An Introduction to the Amstrad PC's	£5.95
BP198	An Introduction to Antenna Theory	£2.95
BP230	A Concise Introduction to GEM	£2.95
BP232	A Concise Introduction to MS-DOS	£2.95
BP233	Electronic Hobbyists Handbook	£4.95
BP239	Getting the Most From Your Multimeter	£2.95
BP240	Remote Control Handbook	£3.95
BP243	BBC BASIC86 on the Amstrad PC's & IBM Compatibles – Book 1: Language	£3.95
BP244	BBC BASIC86 on the Amstrad PC's & IBM Compatibles – Book 2: Graphics and Disk Files	£3.95
BP245	Digital Audio Projects	£2.95
BP246	Musical Applications of the Atari ST's	£5.95
BP247	More Advanced MIDI Projects	£2.95
BP248	Test Equipment Construction	£2.95
BP249	More Advanced Test Equipment Construction	£3.50
BP250	Programming in FORTRAN 77	£4.95
BP251	Computer Hobbyists Handbook	£5.95
BP254	From Atoms to Amperes	£3.50
BP255	International Radio Stations Guide (Revised 1991/92 Edition)	£5.95
BP256	An Introduction to Loudspeakers & Enclosure Design	£2.95
BP257	An Introduction to Amateur Radio	£3.50
BP258	Learning to Program in C (Revised Edition)	£4.95
BP259	A Concise Introduction to UNIX	£2.95
BP260	A Concise Introduction to OS/2	£2.95
BP261	A Concise Introduction to Lotus 1-2-3 (Revised Edition)	£3.95

BP262	A Concise Introduction to Wordperfect (Revised Edition)	£3.95
BP264	A Concise Advanced User's Guide to MS-DOS (Revised Edition)	£3.95
BP265	More Advanced Uses of the Multimeter	£2.95
BP266	Electronic Modules and Systems for Beginners	£3.95
BP267	How to Use Oscilloscopes & Other Test Equipment	£3.50
BP269	An Introduction to Desktop Publishing	£5.95
BP270	A Concise Introduction to Symphony	£3.95
BP271	How to Expand, Modernise & Repair PC's & Compatibles	£4.95
BP272	Interfacing PC's and Compatibles	£3.95
BP273	Practical Electronic Sensors	£4.95
BP274	A Concise Introduction to SuperCalc5	£3.95
BP275	Simple Short Wave Receiver Construction	£3.95
BP276	Short Wave Superhet Receiver Construction	£2.95
BP277	High Power Audio Amplifier Construction	£3.95
BP278	Experimental Antenna Topics	£3.50
BP279	A Concise Introduction to Excel	£3.95
BP280	Getting the Most From Your PC's Hard Disk	£3.95
BP281	An Introduction to VHF/UHF for Radio Amateurs	£3.50
BP282	Understanding PC Specifications	£3.95
BP283	A Concise Introduction to SmartWare II	£4.95
BP284	Programming in QuickBASIC	£4.95
BP285	A Beginners Guide to Modern Electronic Components	£3.95
BP286	A Reference Guide to Basic Electronics Terms	£5.95
BP287	A Reference Guide to Practical Electronics Terms	£5.95
BP288	A Concise Introduction to Windows3.0	£3.95
BP290	An Introduction to Amateur Communications Satellite	£3.95
BP291	A Concise Introduction to Ventura	£3.95
BP292	Public Address Loudspeaker Systems	£3.95
BP293	An Introduction to Radio Wave Propagation	£3.95
BP294	A Concise Introduction to Microsoft Works	£4.95
BP295	A Concise Introduction to Word for Windows	£4.95
BP297	Loudspeakers for Musicians	£3.95
BP298	A Concise Introduction to the Mac System & Finder	£4.95
BP299	Practical Electronic Filters	£4.95
BP300	Setting Up An Amateur Radio Station	£3.95
BP301	Antennas for VHF and UHF	£3.95
BP302	A Concise Users Guide to Lotus 1-2-3 Release 3.1	£3.95
BP303	Understanding PC Software	£4.95
BP304	Projects for Radio Amateurs and SWLs	£3.95
BP305	Learning CAD with AutoSketch for Windows	£5.95
BP306	A Concise Introduction to Ami Pro 3	£4.95
BP307	A Concise Introduction to QuarkXPress	£4.95
BP308	A Concise Introduction to Word 5.1 on the Macintosh	£5.95
BP309	Preamplifier and Filter Circuits	£3.95
BP310	Acoustic Feedback – How to Avoid It	£3.95
BP311	An Introduction to Scanners and Scanning	£4.95
BP312	An Introduction to Microwaves	£3.95
BP313	A Concise Introduction to Sage	£3.95
BP314	A Concise Introduction to Quattro Pro	£4.95
BP315	An Introduction to the Electromagnetic Wave	£4.95
BP316	Practical Electronic Design Data	£4.95
BP317	Practical Electronic Timing	£4.95
BP318	A Concise User's Guide to MS-DOS 5	£4.95
BP319	Making MS-DOS Work for You	£4.95
BP320	Electronic Projects for Your PC	£3.95
BP321	Circuit Source – Book 1	£4.95
BP322	Circuit Source – Book 2	£4.95
BP323	How to Choose a Small Business Computer System	£4.95
BP324	The Art of Soldering	£3.95
BP325	A Concise Users Guide to Windows3.1	£4.95
BP326	The Electronics of Satellite Communications	£4.95
BP327	MS-DOS One Step at a Time	£4.95
BP328	Sage Explained	£5.95
BP329	Electronic Music Learning Projects	£4.95
BP330	A Concise User's Guide to Lotus 1-2-3 Release 2.4	£4.95
BP331	A Beginners Guide to MIDI	£4.95
BP332	A Beginners Guide to TTL Digital ICs	£4.95
BP333	A Beginners Guide to CMOS Digital ICs	£4.95
BP334	Magic Electronic Projects	£4.95
BP335	Operational Amplifier User's Handbook	£5.95
BP336	A Concise User's Guide to Lotus 1-2-3 Release 3.4	£5.95
BP337	A Concise Users Guide to Lotus 1-2-3 for Windows	£5.95
BP338	A Concise Introduction to Word for Windows	£5.95
BP339	A Concise Introduction to Wordperfect 5.2 for Windows	£5.95
BP340	A Concise Introduction to dBase V	£4.95
BP341	A Concise Users Guide to MS-DOS 6	£5.95
BP342	A Conciser Users Guide to Lotus Improv	£5.95